APPLIED PROCESS CONTROL

CONTROL

A CASE STUDY

R. B. NEWELL
and
P. L. LEE

Process Control Group
Department of Chemical Engineering
University of Queensland
Brisbane, Australia

PRENTICE HALL

New York   London   Toronto   Sydney   Tokyo

Prentice Hall, Inc., *Englewood Cliffs, New Jersey*
Prentice Hall of Australia Pty Ltd, *Sydney*
Prentice Hall Canada, Inc., *Toronto*
Prentice Hall Hispanoamericana, S.A., *Mexico*
Prentice Hall of India Private Ltd, *New Delhi*
Prentice Hall International, Inc., *London*
Prentice Hall of Japan, Inc., *Tokyo*
Prentice Hall of Southeast Asia Pty Ltd, *Singapore*
Editora Prentice Hall do Brasil Ltda, *Rio de Janeiro*

Typeset in Australia by Monoset Typesetters, Strathpine, Qld
Printed and bound in Australia by Brown Prior Anderson Pty Ltd, Burwood, Victoria

Cover design by Kim Webber

1 2 3 4 5 93 92 91 90 89
ISBN 0-13-040940-5

National Library of Australia
Cataloguing-in-Publication Data

Newell, R. B. (Robert B.), 1943–
  Applied process control.

  Includes index.
  ISBN 0-13-040940-5

  1. Process control. 2. Control theory—
  Computer programs. I. Lee, Peter, 1954–
  II. Title.

629.8′312

Library of Congress
Cataloguing-in-Publication Data

Newell, R. B., 1943–
  Applied process control: a case study/R. B. Newell and P. L. Lee.
    p. cm.
  ISBN 0-13-040940-5
  1. Chemical process control. 2. Evaporators. I. Lee, P. L.,
1954–   . II. Title.
TP155.75.N48 1988
660.2′81—dc19   88-18837
                                                          CIP

PRENTICE HALL

A division of Simon & Schuster

Contents

TP155
.75
N48
1989

CHEM

Preface

This book is *not* yet another textbook on process control. It *is* a book of *case studies* describing the application of a variety of process control techniques to a single process. These techniques cover a wide range, including identification, PID control, predictive control and fuzzy control. The process is a highly interacting forced-circulation evaporator. The book is intended to be a *teaching* book and is in no way a research monograph.

The *objective* of the book is to be a practical support text for courses in process control (undergraduate, postgraduate, or continuing education) and could be the basis for a process control laboratory course.

The book is intended as an aid to prospective and practicing chemical engineers, or to other plant engineers who become involved in process control. It is not intended for the specialist process control engineer, although hopefully they too will find it of interest. As a result the design techniques are all presented in the time domain. The reader will discover ordinary differential equations, difference equations and matrices and vectors. The reader will not find Laplace transforms, either to their delight or horror depending upon their basic beliefs.

Readers are assumed to have done (or to be doing) at least a reasonable first course in process modeling and process control at the undergraduate level. Textbooks such as Smith and Corripio (1985) and Stephanopoulus (1984) can be referred to for basic material if needed. Some difficult-to-find support material is included as appendices. Particularly in the later chapters, a more advanced undergraduate course or a graduate course in so-called "modern control theory" would be of assistance. There are numerous textbooks in this area of which your library will have a selection.

The forced-circulation vertical-tube evaporator used throughout this book is described in Chapter 2. At first sight, this would appear a trivial process upon which to base a book of case studies for a wide variety of control techniques. Certainly this process limits presentation to problems of essentially three dimensions, although in the teaching situation most students would consider that quite sufficient. However, on closer examination it will be found that the process is highly interacting and tests to the limit even the more sophisticated control techniques.

Various exercises are given in addition to the case studies. For the most part these are not trivial exercises and will take the reader some considerable time to complete. There is a large amount of support software available as well as various simulations of the evaporator (see Appendix A).

The many plots that show the performance of different control strategies in this book were produced with the aid of the support software described in Appendix A. These plots show *scaled* values of both the input and output variables. The scaling used for each variable was as follows:

Actual	Scaled
0	0
Steady state	50%
2*Steady state	100%

References

Smith, C. A. and Corripio, A. B. (1985), *Principles and Practice of Automatic Process Control*, Wiley, New York.

Stephanopoulos, G. (1984), *Chemical Process Control—An Introduction to Theory and Practice*. Prentice Hall. Englewood Cliffs. NJ.

1 Discrete time systems

1.1 Introduction

Modern process control is usually implemented using microprocessor-based control equipment. Such devices "sample" process measurements at discrete intervals in time and take control actions, usually at the "sample rate". In practice, digital control systems use relatively high sampling rates so that they approximate continuous systems, but sampled-data effects can still be quite important in many instances.

As this book is aimed at the practicing plant engineer, many of the techniques presented in this book are described in the time-domain rather than the Laplace-domain. However, it will be required to express some process models and design techniques in a mathematical form that will be easily implemented by digital control systems. The techniques used in this book include the forward shift operator q or a z-transform, both of which will be introduced in this chapter. The book by Astrom and Wittenmark (1984) is an excellent text in this area and is recommended for clarification and the study of discrete systems in more depth.

1.2 System models

All control design techniques depend to a lesser or greater extent upon a mathematical model of the process to be controlled. This model may vary from a complex mechanistic model to a simple empirical model. Both types will be encountered in the case studies in this book.

State equation models

Mechanistic models are made up of a number of conservation balances and constitutive or empirical relations. The conservation balances are generally mass and energy balances for chemical processes and take the form of ordinary differential equations. The constitutive relations describe kinetic and rate processes and property dependencies

1

and are usually algebraic in nature. These equations are generally simplified for control system design and presented in the form of a "state equation":

$$dx/dt = f(x, u, d)$$

where: x is the state vector and defines the mass and energy inventories or "state" of the process.

u is the vector of manipulated variables affecting the process.

d is the vector of disturbance variables.

f is in general a vector of some nonlinear function.

Often it is desirable to express the variables in normalized perturbation form:

$$z_n = (z - z_{ss})/z_{ss}$$

where: z_n is the normalized value of the particular variable.

z_{ss} is the steady-state value of the variable.

In many design techniques the state equation is linearized and parameters assumed time invariant, giving the equation:

$$dx/dt = Ax + Bu + Dd$$

where: A is the state matrix.

B is the control matrix.

D is the disturbance matrix.

The constant matrices may be obtained from the original nonlinear model by evaluating the Jacobians as:

$$A = \left[\frac{\delta f_i}{\delta x_i}\right]$$

$$B = \left[\frac{\delta f_i}{\delta u_i}\right]$$

$$D = \left[\frac{\delta f_i}{\delta d_i}\right]$$

The state equation is often accompanied by the "output equation":

$$y = g(x)$$

or:

$$y = Cx$$

where y is a vector of output variables or measurements.

The discrete state equation

The nature of digital computers means that control systems use discrete-time values of process outputs y and generate discrete-time values of process manipulated variables u.

The sensors attached to the computer may supply discrete-time measurements (e.g.

a gas chromatograph) but usually the computer interface samples a continuous sensor signal. In this book only fixed rate sampling every T_s times unit will be considered. T_s is known as the sampling time. The sampling process is complex and the sampling rate determines the amount of useful information obtained from the continuous signal. For a full discussion, refer to Astrom and Wittenmark (1984).

The discrete values of the control actions generated by the computer must generally be converted to a continuous control valve signal. This is invariably done by holding the output value constant until the next value comes along. This process is known as a zero order hold and in some cases must be "modeled" with the process.

The discrete linear state and output equations can be written in the following form:

$$\underset{\sim}{x}_{k+1} = \underset{\sim}{\Phi} \underset{\sim}{x}_k + \underset{\sim}{\Delta} \underset{\sim}{u}_{12_k} + \underset{\sim}{\Theta} \underset{\sim}{d}_k$$
$$y_k = \underset{\sim}{C} \underset{\sim}{x}_k$$

where $\underset{\sim}{x}_{k+1}$ and $\underset{\sim}{x}_k$ represent the discrete values of state vector $\underset{\sim}{x}$ at times t_{k+1} and t_k where:

$$t_{k+1} = t_k + T_s$$

The discrete and continuous state, control and disturbance matrices are related by:

$$\underset{\sim}{\Phi} = e^{\underset{\sim}{A}T_s}$$

$$\underset{\sim}{\Delta} = e^{\underset{\sim}{A}T_s} \left[\int_o^{T_s} e^{-\underset{\sim}{A}\tau} d\tau \right] \underset{\sim}{B}$$

$$\underset{\sim}{\Theta} = e^{\underset{\sim}{A}T_s} \left[\int_o^{T_s} e^{-\underset{\sim}{A}\tau} d\tau \right] \underset{\sim}{D}$$

The simplest way to evaluate the matrix exponential is by the series expansion:

$$e^{\underset{\sim}{A}t} = \underset{\sim}{I} + \underset{\sim}{A}t + (\underset{\sim}{A}t)^2 + (\underset{\sim}{A}t)^3 + \dots$$

Input-output models

Empirical models are generally in the form of "input-output" equations:

$$y = f(u)$$

Whereas state equation models represent a full description of the process, input-output models simply describe the relationship between an output and one or more inputs. Input-output equations can be derived from the state equation by simplification, but in general the reverse is not true.

The discrete linear input-output model can be written in the following general form:

$$y_k + a_1 y_{k-1} + a_2 y_{k-2} + \dots = b_0 u_k + b_1 u_{k-1} + b_2 u_{k-2} + \dots$$

1.3 The difference operator

The forward shift operator q is defined by the relation:

$$x_{k+1} = q x_k$$

It is also used as a backward shift operator q^{-1} where:

$$q^{-1}x_k = x_{k-1}$$

Input-output models are often written in terms of q or q^{-1}, for example:

$$y_k(1 + a_1q^{-1} + a_2q^{-2} + \ldots) = u_k(b_0 + b_1q^{-1} + b_2q^{-2} + \ldots)$$

or as:

$$y_kA(q^{-1}) = u_kB(q^{-1})$$

where $A(\ )$ and $B(\ )$ are polynomials in q^{-1}.

The input-output model is also often written as:

$$y_k = \frac{B(q^{-1})}{A(q^{-1})} u_k$$

although in general it is only valid to divide out the polynomials if y_k and u_k represent deviation variables with zero initial conditions.

The ratio $B(\ )/A(\ )$ is known as the "pulse transfer operator" $H(\ )$.

1.4 The z-transform

The z-transform is the discrete equivalent of the Laplace transform and is defined by the equation:

$$F(z) = \sum_{k=0}^{\infty} (f_k z^{-k})$$

Applying this to the discrete state equation and assuming zero initial conditions gives:

$$z\underset{\sim}{X}(z) = \underset{\sim}{\Phi}\underset{\sim}{X}(z) + \underset{\sim}{\Delta}\underset{\sim}{U}(z)$$

or:

$$\underset{\sim}{X}(z) = (z\underset{\sim}{I} - \underset{\sim}{\Phi})^{-1}\underset{\sim}{\Delta}\underset{\sim}{U}(z)$$

The pulse transfer function $H(z) = Y(z)/U(z)$ is identical to the pulse transfer operator with q replaced by z. However, the variable z is a complex variable and not an operator.

Standard block diagram manipulations can be carried out using z-transforms of signals and pulse transfer functions to relate transformed signals.

The inversion of z-transforms into the time domain is particularly convenient. The transform is simply divided out into a polynomial in z^{-1} and since z^{-1} is the transform of a time shift, the coefficients of the polynomial are the values at the appropriate discrete times.

1.5 Stability

The simplest test of stability for discrete linear systems is to obtain the eigenvalues of the state matrix or the poles of $H(z)$ (the roots of the characteristic equation $A(z) = 0$).

A system is stable if the outputs remain bounded for bounded inputs and bounded initial conditions. A linear system is *stable* if all eigenvalues or poles lie on or within the "unit circle", that is, their absolute values are equal to or less than unity.

A system is *asymptotically stable* if it is stable and if the outputs approach a steady state as time approaches infinity for bounded initial conditions. A linear system is asymptotically stable if all eigenvalues or poles lie within the "unit circle", that is, their absolute values are less than unity.

In general, control systems are designed to be asymptotically stable.

1.6 Exercises

1. A constant volume stirred tank is heated by steam condensing in a coil. The energy balance is:

$$10 dT/dt = 2T_i + Q - 2T$$

and the heat transfer relation is:

$$Q = 2(100 - T)$$

where: T is the temperature in the tank.
T_i is the temperature of the inlet stream.
Q is the amount of heat transferred to the tank per unit time.
t is time.

(a) Write this model in the state equation form using perturbation variables.
(b) Write this model in discrete form where $T_s = 0.2$.
(c) Write as an input-output model between T and Q.
(d) Write down the corresponding pulse transfer function.
(e) Show that the process is stable.
(f) Show that the closed-loop system is stable with a proportional controller of gain 10. Calculate the gain at which the closed-loop process would be unstable.

2. A pure salt is added to water flowing through two tanks in series as shown:

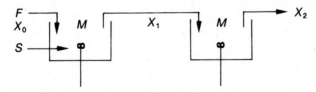

F and S are mass flowrates.
M is mass.
X is mass fraction.

Assume the tanks to be well mixed, of constant volume and of equal size.
(a) Write down the appropriate conservation balances.
(b) Write the state and output equations using perturbation variables where the output is X_2
(c) Write the model in discrete form, where: $F = 2.$
$$M = 10.$$
$$T_s = 0.5.$$
(d) Write as an input-output model between X_2 and S.
(e) Write down the corresponding pulse transfer function.
(f) Show that the process is stable.
(g) Show that the closed-loop system is stable with a proportional controller of gain 10. Calculate the gain at which the closed-loop process would be unstable.

1.7 References

Astrom, K. J. and Wittenmark, B. (1984), *Computer Controlled Systems: Theory and Design*, Prentice Hall, Englewood Cliffs, NJ.

2 The evaporator model

2.1 Introduction

The concentration of dilute liquors by evaporating solvent from the feed stream is an important industrial process used in such industries as sugar mills, alumina production and paper manufacture, to name a few. An often used evaporator, known as a "forced circulation evaporator", is shown in Figure 2.1. In this evaporator, feed is mixed with a

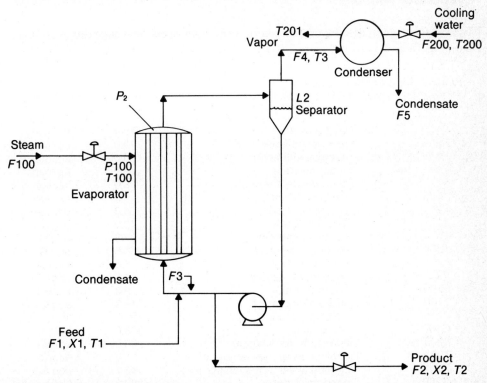

Figure 2.1 Evaporator system

7

high volumetric flowrate of recirculating liquor and is pumped into a vertical heat exchanger. Often the heat exchanger is heated with steam which condenses on the outside of the tube walls. The liquor which passes up the inside of the tubes, boils and then passes to a separation vessel. In this vessel, liquid and vapor are separated. The liquid is recirculated with some being drawn off as product. The vapor is usually condensed by cooling, with water often being used as the coolant.

This chapter derives a mathematical model of a forced circulation evaporator. There are two major parts to this description of the mathematical model:

- The first part derives a mechanistic nonlinear model with major assumptions stated, variables defined and parameters given.
- The second part derives a linear state space description in normalized form by evaluating the appropriate Jacobian elements.

2.2 The nonlinear model

Evaporator variables

The variable names, descriptions, standard steady state values, and engineering units are shown in Table 2.1 and in Figure 2.1. The solvent is water and the solute is nonvolatile.

Table 2.1 Evaporator variables

Variable	Description	Value	Units
$F1$	feed flowrate	10.0	kg/min
$F2$	product flowrate	2.0	kg/min
$F3$	circulating flowrate	50.0	kg/min
$F4$	vapor flowrate	8.0	kg/min
$F5$	condensate flowrate	8.0	kg/min
$X1$	feed composition	5.0	percent
$X2$	product composition	25.0	percent
$T1$	feed temperature	40.0	deg C
$T2$	product temperature	84.6	deg C
$T3$	vapor temperature	80.6	deg C
$L2$	separator level	1.0	metres
$P2$	operating pressure	50.5	kPa
$F100$	steam flowrate	9.3	kg/min
$T100$	steam temperature	119.9	deg C
$P100$	steam pressure	194.7	kPa
$Q100$	heater duty	339.0	kW
$F200$	cooling water flowrate	208.0	kg/min
$T200$	cooling water inlet temperature	25.0	deg C
$T201$	cooling water outlet temperature	46.1	deg C
$Q200$	condenser duty	307.9	kW

Process liquid mass balance

A mass balance on the total process liquid (solvent and solute) in the system yields:

$$\rho A \, dL2/dt = F1 - F4 - F2 \tag{2.1}$$

where: ρ is the liquid density.

A is the cross-sectional area of the separator.

The product ρA is assumed to be constant at 20 kg/metre.

Process liquid solute mass balance

A mass balance on the solute in the process liquid phase yields:

$$M \, dX2/dt = F1 \, X1 - F2 \, X2 \tag{2.2}$$

where M is the amount of liquid in the evaporator and is assumed to be constant at 20 kg.

Process vapor mass balance

A mass balance on the process vapor in the evaporator will express the total mass of the water vapor in terms of the pressure that exists in the system:

$$C \, dP2/dt = F4 - F5 \tag{2.3}$$

where C is a constant that converts the mass of vapor into an equivalent pressure and is assumed to have a value of 4 kg/kPa. This constant can be derived from the ideal gas law.

Process liquid energy balance

The process liquid is assumed to always exist at its boiling point and to be perfectly mixed (assisted by the high circulation rate).

The liquid temperature is:

$$T2 = 0.5616 \, P2 + 0.3126 \, X2 + 48.43 \tag{2.4}$$

which is a linearization of the saturated liquid line for water about the standard steady-state value and includes a term to approximate boiling point elevation due to the presence of the solute.

The vapor temperature is:

$$T3 = 0.507 \, P2 + 55.0 \tag{2.5}$$

which is a linearization of the saturated liquid line for water about the standard steady-state value.

The dynamics of the energy balance are assumed to be very fast so that:

$$F4 = (Q100 - F1\,C_P\,(T2 - T1))/\lambda \tag{2.6}$$

where C_P is the heat capacity of the liquor and is assumed constant at a value of 0.07 kW/K (kg/min) and λ is the latent heat of vaporization of the liquor and is assumed to have a constant value of 38.5 kW/(kg/min).

The sensible heat change between $T2$ and $T3$ for $F4$ is considered small compared to the latent heat. It is assumed that there are no heat losses to the environment or heat gains from the energy input of the pump.

Heater steam jacket

Steam pressure $P100$ is a manipulated variable which determines steam temperature under assumed saturated conditions. An equation relating steam temperature to steam pressure can be obtained by approximating the saturated steam temperature–pressure relationship by local linearization about the steady-state value:

$$T100 = 0.1538\,P100 + 90.0 \tag{2.7}$$

The rate of heat transfer to the boiling process liquid is given by:

$$Q100 = UA1\,(T100 - T2) \tag{2.8}$$

where $UA1$ is the overall heat transfer coefficient times the heat transfer area and is a function of the total flowrate through the tubes in the evaporator:

$$UA1 = 0.16\,(F1 + F3)$$

The steam flowrate is calculated from:

$$F100 = Q100/\lambda_s \tag{2.9}$$

where λ_s is the latent heat of steam at the saturated conditions, assumed constant at a value of 36.6 kW/(kg/min).

The dynamics within the steam jacket have been assumed to be very fast.

Condenser

The cooling water flowrate $F200$ is a manipulated variable and the inlet temperature $T200$ is a disturbance variable.

A cooling water energy balance yields:

$$Q200 = F200\,C_P\,(T201 - T200)$$

where C_P is the heat capacity of the cooling water assumed constant at 0.07 kW/(kg/min).

The heat transfer rate equation is approximated by:

$$Q200 = UA2\,(T3 - 0.5\,(T200 + T201))$$

where $UA2$ is the overall heat transfer coefficient times the heat transfer area, which is assumed constant with a value of 6.84 kW/K.

These two equations can be combined to eliminate $T201$ to give explicitly:

$$Q200 = \frac{UA2\,(T3 - T200)}{1 + UA2/(2\ C_P\ F200)} \tag{2.10}$$

It follows that:

$$T201 = T200 + Q200/(F200\ C_P) \tag{2.11}$$

The condensate flowrate is:

$$F5 = Q200/\lambda \tag{2.12}$$

where λ is the latent heat of vaporization of water assumed constant at 38.5 kW/K(kg/min).

The dynamics within the condenser have been assumed to be very fast.

Degrees of freedom

In any modeling and control problem, it is advisable to check that the problem is well formulated. This can be achieved by performing a degrees of freedom analysis. If the degrees of freedom of the problem is equal to zero, then the problem is well posed and a unique solution of the problem is possible.

For this problem there are 20 variables, which are shown in Table 2.1. There are 12 equations defined above. Therefore:

DOF = Number of variables − Number of equations
  = 20 − 12
  = 8

This implies that eight extra pieces of information need to be supplied to define a unique solution. This is achieved by specifying the input variables as follows:

3 manipulated variables ($F2$, $P100$, $F200$)
5 disturbance variables ($F3$, $F1$, $X1$, $T1$, $T200$)

With these variables assigned values, the problem has zero degrees of freedom and a unique solution is possible.

Nonlinear model implementations

Several implementations of the nonlinear model are currently available:

1. a FORTRAN subroutine;
2. an IBM Advanced Control System simulation;
3. a SPEEDUP simulation model;
4. a Bailey Network 90 simulation;
5. a FIX simulation.

Information on the availability of software can be found in Appendix A.

In the implementations, process controllers are included on the manipulated variables $F2$, $P100$, $F200$ and the recirculating flowrate $F3$. These controllers would act as slave controllers to any process control scheme and are added to make the simulation more "realistic", making instantaneous changes in these variables impossible. The dynamics of these control loops are approximated by first-order lags with time constants of 1.2 minutes.

2.3 The linear model

The Jacobian matrices

The linear model is derived from the nonlinear state space model:

$$dx/dt = f(x, u, d)$$

by making a Taylor Series expansion about a steady state and considering only the first order terms:

$$dx_p/dt = Ax_p + Bu_p + Dd_p$$

where: the subscript p denotes a perturbation variable (e.g. $x_p = x - x_{ss}$, where x_{ss} is the steady state).

Matrices A, B and D are the Jacobians of $f()$ with regard to x, u and d respectively.

The individual elements in terms of steady state values are listed in Appendix B.

The variables are then normalized by substituting:

$$x_p = x_n x_{ss}$$

where: x_n are the normalized variables.

x_{ss} are steady state values.

For the standard steady states listed in Table 2.1 the Jacobians in normalized perturbation form are:

$$A = \begin{bmatrix} 0 & 0.10445 & 0.37935 \\ 0 & -0.1 & 0 \\ 0 & -0.10340 \times 10^{-1} & -0.54738 \times 10^{-1} \end{bmatrix}$$

$$B = \begin{bmatrix} -0.1 & 0.37266 & 0 \\ -0.1 & 0 & 0 \\ 0 & 0.36914 \times 10^{-1} & -0.75272 \times 10^{-2} \end{bmatrix}$$

$$D = \begin{bmatrix} -0.36676 & 0.38605 & 0 & -0.36360 \times 10^{-1} & 0 \\ 0 & 0.1 & 0.1 & 0 & 0 \\ 0.36302 \times 10^{-1} & 0.32268 \times 10^{-2} & 0 & 0.35972 \times 10^{-2} & 0.17785 \times 10^{-1} \end{bmatrix}$$

where $\underset{\sim}{x}$, $\underset{\sim}{u}$ and $\underset{\sim}{d}$ are defined as:

$$\underset{\sim}{x}^{\mathrm{T}} = [L2 \; X2 \; P2]$$
$$\underset{\sim}{u}^{\mathrm{T}} = [F2 \; P100 \; F200]$$
$$\underset{\sim}{d}^{\mathrm{T}} = [F3 \; F1 \; X1 \; T1 \; T200]$$

2.4 Exercises

1. Write a FORTRAN program to evaluate the dynamic response of the evaporator to a step change in a selected manipulated or disturbance variable.

2. Obtain the response of the system states to step changes of 20 percent in the feed concentration.

3. Determine the steady state of the process for a 20 percent reduction in steam pressure $P100$.

4. Determine the values of the Jacobians for a linear state space model at the new steady state determined in Exercise 3.

3 Process identification techniques

3.1 Introduction

In many practical situations a model of the process is not available and not economic, or even necessary, to derive. Even if a model is available, as in this case (Chapter 2), it may be desirable to represent the process much more simply than by a full nonlinear or linear state-space model.

This chapter will present two process identification techniques. The first is the traditional and very simple step test procedure. The second is a modern and more sophisticated technique called time series analysis. Both of these techniques can be used to derive an input-output model of the process.

3.2 General principles

There are basically three steps to any identification procedure:

1. Collect input-output response data from the process (or from a more complex model) after applying a suitable stimulus to the input.
2. Propose a form of model to represent the process usually dependent upon the use to be made of the model.
3. Fit the model to the data to determine the parameters of the model.

Data collection

It is necessary during the process tests to eliminate, as far as possible, other stimuli to the process. All identification techniques are susceptible to such data corruption.

It is also necessary to apply a "suitable" stimuli to the process input. It must be:

1. the correct form for the analysis procedure;
2. of sufficient magnitude to give a reasonable signal to noise ratio at the process output;
3. stimulating at all the frequencies of interest.

If you are in doubt about the frequency content of the stimulus then you can apply the following test:

$$\text{frequency content} = \frac{|F(u, \omega)|}{|F(u, 0)|} > 0.3$$

for: $0 < \omega < 5/t_{min}$

where: u is the stimulus signal.

         ω is the frequency (radians/sec).

         $F(\ )$ is the Fourier transform.

         t_{min} is the smallest time constant of interest (sec).

A FORTRAN program is available to calculate the frequency content (see Appendix A).

It is also necessary to collect values of input u and output y at a sufficiently high frequency to avoid aliasing at the maximum frequency of interest. Aliasing is a form of data corruption due to the discrete sampling process (Astrom and Wittenmark 1984). For most normal types of stimuli use the test:

$$0.3\omega_s > 5/t_{min}$$

where: ω_s is the sampling frequency $(2\pi/T_s)$.

         T_s is the sampling interval.

which implies that:

$$T_s < 0.38t_{min}$$

The final question concerns the length of time for which data should be collected. The answer depends to some extent upon the analysis procedure, but in general, collect data for a time greater than three or four times the largest time constant of interest.

The model form

There is much debate over how complex a model can reasonably be identified from experimental data. It is obviously dependent upon the data quality (accuracy, corruption, noise, etc.) and the analysis technique.

The cautious will say that the most that can be expected is a first order plus deadtime model (FOPDT) of the form:

$$y(t)(1 + a_1 q^{-1}) = b_0 u(t - D)$$

where: $a_1 = -\tau/(\tau + T_s)$

         $b_0 = KT_s/(\tau + T_s)$

         K = process gain

         τ = process time constant

         D = process deadtime

         q^{-1} = a backward shift operator

The optimistic will say that the most that can be expected is a second order plus deadtime (SOPDT) model of the form:

$$y(t)(1 + a_1 q^{-1} + a_2 q^{-2)} = b_0 u(t - D)$$

where: $a_1 = -2(\tau + T_s)/(\tau^2 + 2\zeta\tau T_s + T_s^2)$

$a_2 = \tau^2/(\tau^2 + 2\zeta\tau T_s + T_s^2)$

$b_0 = KT_s^2/(\tau^2 + 2\zeta\tau T_s + T_s^2)$

ζ = process damping ratio

3.3 The step test

The step test is, in practice, probably the most frequently applied process identification technique.

The frequency content of a step is shown in Figure 3.1. This assumes a perfect step, that is, right angle corners. It can be shown that the 0.3 frequency cut-off is approximately related to the rise time of the step by:

$$\omega_{cut-off} = 0.0196/\text{rise-time}$$

which should be greater than $5/t_{min}$ (see Section 3.2). For example, to identify a 5 minute time constant, the rise time must be faster than 1.1 seconds. Approximate steps often have a much lower frequency content and should be tested.

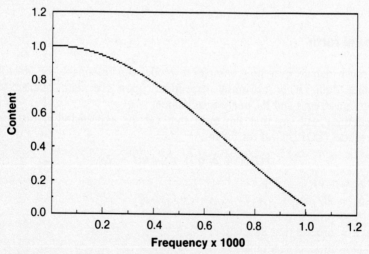

Figure 3.1 Frequency content of a step

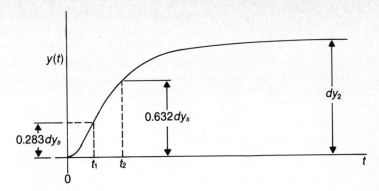

Figure 3.2 Fitting a FOPDT to a step response

Once a step response has been obtained it is then necessary to determine the model parameters.

Possibly the best manual technique for a FOPDT model is that due to C. L. Smith (1972). Two times are measured from the response (as shown in Figure 3.2):

$$t_1 \text{ when } dy = 0.283dy_s$$
$$t_2 \text{ when } dy = 0.632dy_s$$

where: dy is the change in output at t_1 or t_2.
dy_s is the steady state change in output.

then:

$$K = \text{gain} = dy_s/du_s$$

$$\tau = \text{time constant} = 1.5(t_2 - t_1)$$

$$D = \text{deadtime} = t_2 - \tau$$

unless D is negative in which case: $\tau = t_2$

$$D = 0$$

An optimization technique can be used to determine the best parameters in the least squares sense. Care must be taken, as the response surface is seldom well behaved and a good first estimate is essential (e.g. by using Smith's manual technique).

General consensus holds that it is not possible to reliably fit a SOPDT model to a step response, although the method of Oldenberg and Sartorius (1948) can be used.

3.4 Step tests on the evaporator

In order to demonstrate some of the points discussed and some problems frequently encountered, step testing of the nonlinear evaporator model was carried out. The objective was to obtain FOPDT models for the effect of feed flowrate $F1$ on the operating pressure *P2* and the product composition *X2*. Separator level *L2* was controlled by adjusting the exit flowrate *F2*. This control loop is necessary to ensure that the remainder of the evaporator system is open-loop bounded.

Since the model is nonlinear it is important to keep the step size as small as possible while still maintaining some accuracy. It is also necessary to examine both increases and decreases in the input *F1*. A step size of ten percent was chosen.

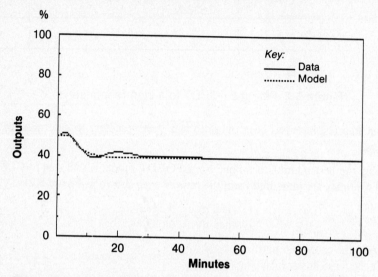

Figure 3.3 *X2* response to increase in *F1*

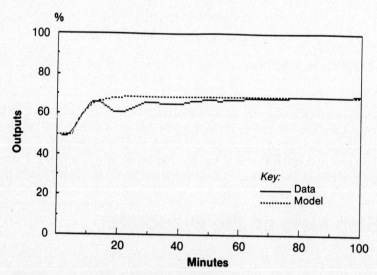

Figure 3.4 *X2* response to decrease in *F1*

Sample responses are shown in Figures 3.3 and 3.4. Note that the responses are oscillatory so that the FOPDT model will be a very rough approximation.

The application of Smith's technique resulted in the parameters shown in Table 3.1.

Table 3.1 Step test: Parameter estimates

		Gain	*Time constant*	*Deadtime*
P2	F1 incr.	2.66	26.4	4.6
	F1 decr.	3.44	36.4	3.6
	Average	3.05	31.4	4.1
X2	F1 incr.	−6.30	3.3	5.6
	F1 decr.	−8.44	3.9	5.7
	Average	−7.37	3.6	5.6

The effect of the nonlinearities in the model are quite evident even for the relatively small step size.

Using these values as a starting point, an optimization technique was used to give refined estimates in the least squares sense. The results appear in Table 3.2 and were in reasonable agreement.

Table 3.2 Step test: Optimized parameter estimates

		Gain	*Time constant*	*Deadtime*
P2	Smith	3.05	31.4	4.1
	Least Squares	3.00	27.6	6.0
X2	Smith	−7.37	3.6	5.6
	Least Squares	−6.70	2.5	6.0

3.5 Time series analysis

The facet of Time Series Analysis (TSA) of interest in this context is its application to process identification. The more glamorous facet is in the art of forecasting, for example forecasting the price of stocks and shares. The problem can be posed as: "Given a sequence of input values (a time series) and a sequence of output values from a process, how can a model of the process be determined?" The input and output sequences can often be obtained from normal operating data, if the frequency content of the input time series is suitable (see Section 3.3).

The "authority" on Time Series Analysis is the book by Box and Jenkins (1970) from which the following material has been extracted. This account is considered the minimum background sufficient to use one of the TSA software packages available (see Appendix A).

Identification procedure

The general form of a TSA process model is shown in Figure 3.5. There are basically three models to be determined:

1. The input model describes the input time series $u(t)$ in terms of white noise $a(t)$.
2. The process model is the main process description and describes the effect the process has on the input time series. This is the model of major interest.
3. The residuals or noise model describes the residuals between the output signal from the process model and the actual measured time series $y(t)$, again in terms of white noise $a(t)$.

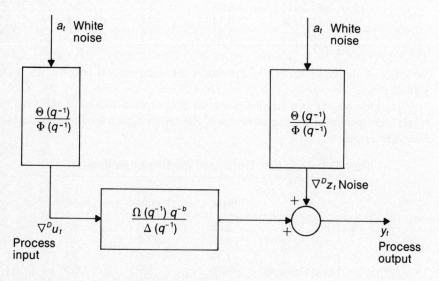

Figure 3.5 Time series analysis process model

All three models are of the form of an autoregressive integrated moving average (ARIMA) model. For example the form of the input and residuals models is:

$$\Phi(q^{-1}) \, \nabla^D \, z(t) = \theta_0 + \Theta(q^{-1}) \, a(t)$$

where $\Phi(q^{-1})$ and $\Theta(q^{-1})$ are polynomials in the backward shift operator q^{-1}:

$$\Phi(q^{-1}) = 1 - \phi_1 \, q^{-1} - \ldots - \phi_p \, q^{-p}$$

$$\Theta(q^{-1}) = 1 - \theta_1 \, q^{-1} - \ldots - \theta_q \, q^{-q}$$

$$\nabla^D = (1 - q^{-1})^D$$

and $z(t)$ is the input time series $u(t)$ or the residuals.

The form of the process model is:

$$\Delta(q^{-1}) \, \nabla^{D} \, y(t) = \Omega(q^{-1}) \, u(t - b)$$

where $\Delta(q^{-1})$ and $\Omega(q^{-1})$ are polynomials in q^{-1} of order r and s respectively:

$$\Delta(q^{-1}) = 1 - \delta_1 \, q^{-1} - \ldots - \delta_r \, q^{-r}$$

$$\Omega(q^{-1}) = \omega_0 - \omega_1 \, q^{-1} - \ldots - \omega_s \, q^{-s}$$

The sequence of steps in the identification is as follows:

1. Identify the form of the input model (select the differencing D and orders p and q) from calculated autocorrelations and partial autocorrelations.
2. Estimate the parameters of the input model (this is basically a nonlinear least squares estimation).
3. Identify the form of the process model (select the differencing, deadtime b and orders r and s) from calculated impulse and step responses. Differencing is required if the process is not self-regulatory.
4. Calculate the first estimates of the process parameters from the impulse response.
5. Identify the form of the residuals model (select the differencing D and orders p and q) from calculated autocorrelations and partial autocorrelations.
6. Estimate the parameters of the residuals model (this is basically a nonlinear least squares estimation).
7. Make a final estimation of all parameters.

These are all computer assisted steps. However, there are still three areas of human judgement:

1. interpreting autocorrelations and partial autocorrelations;
2. interpreting impulse and step responses;
3. evaluating the quality of the final estimated model.

These three steps are discussed in more detail in the following sections and in Box and Jenkins (1970). The whole process is illustrated in Section 3.6 by working through an example.

Interpreting autocorrelations and partial autocorrelations

The objective of this interpretation step is to select the form of the ARIMA model which will describe the given time series $z(t)$ in terms of white noise $a(t)$. The form of the ARIMA model is given by:

$$\Phi(q^{-1}) \, \nabla^{D} \, z(t) = \theta_0 + \Theta(q^{-1}) \, a(t)$$

where: D is the degree of differencing required to produce a stationary time series (usually 0, 1 or 2).

p is the order of the $AR(p)$ autoregressive part of the model which is also the order of $\Phi(q^{-1})$.

q is the order of the $MA(q)$ moving average part of the model which is also the order of $\Theta(q^{-1})$.

These values can in part be determined from the form of the two plots of the autocorrelation and the partial autocorrelation against the number of lags.

Firstly, both plots must tail off to within their confidence limits. If either plot does not tail off, then the time series is not stationary, that is, it does not have a constant mean value with time. In this case the series must be differenced, that is, each point is subtracted from the succeeding point:

$$z(t) = z(t + T_s) - z(t)$$

If this is done once or perhaps twice then most practical data will become stationary.

Secondly, the orders p and q of the $AR(p)$ and $MA(q)$ parts of the model must be estimated. There are three possibilities:

1. A pure $AR(p)$ model with $q = 0$. In this case the autocorrelation plot should tail off exponentially and the partial autocorrelation plot should cut off sharply after p lags.
2. A pure $MA(q)$ model with $p = 0$. This is the dual case where the partial autocorrelation plot should tail off exponentially and the autocorrelation plot should cut off sharply after q lags.
3. A mixed $ARMA(p, q)$ model in which both plots tail off exponentially.

The TSA time series software package (see Appendix A) includes a program called AUTO which attempts to implement the above interpretation in a simple rule-based fashion. It is a useful advisory tool but should always be confirmed by examining the plots. It will also admit defeat when the plots do not follow the "usual" patterns.

Interpreting impulse and step responses

The objective of this interpretation step is to select the form of the ARIMA model which will describe the process under investigation. The form of this ARIMA model is:

$$\Delta(q^{-1}) \nabla^D y(t) = \Omega(q^{-1}) u(t - b)$$

where: b is the deadtime before the process responds to a change in $u(t)$.

r is the order of the $AR(r)$ autoregressive part of the model which is also the order of $\Delta(q^{-1})$.

s is the order of the $MA(s)$ moving average part of the model which is also the order of $\Omega(q^{-1})$.

In addition, this interpretation step must also determine whether differencing is required, that is, if the process is not self-regulatory (includes an integrating term).

These values can in part be determined from the form of the two plots of the impulse response and the step response.

Firstly, the step response must settle to a new steady state value and the impulse response tail off to within its confidence limits. If the step response keeps increasing, this indicates that the process is not self-regulatory. In this case the procedure should be repeated with differencing selected.

Secondly, the deadtime can be determined by examining the number of time intervals before both the step and impulse responses become greater than their confidence limits.

Thirdly, the form of the step response must be examined to determine the order r of the process (of the AR term $\Delta(q^{-1})$). Generally it should have one of three general shapes:

1. A step shape with a sharp rise to a steady state value indicating a zero order process.
2. An exponential rise to a new steady state value indicating a first order process.
3. An overshoot past and oscillations around a new steady state value indicating a second order process.

If the process has an overdamped or critically damped second order characteristic, then it will most likely appear to be a first order process with some deadtime. The difference is difficult to distinguish without prior knowledge, for example, it may be known that there is no deadtime in the actual process.

Finally, an estimate is required for the order s of the MA term $\Omega(q^{-1})$. The estimation technique depends upon the AR order r. If r is zero, then s is the number of significant impulse values minus one. If r is one, then s is the number of significant impulse values. If r is two, then s is the number of significant values before the peak on the step response minus one.

The TSA time series software package (see Appendix A) includes a program called IMPULSE which attempts to implement the above interpretation in a simple rule-based fashion. It is a useful advisory tool but should always be confirmed by examining the plots. It will also admit defeat when the plots do not follow the "usual" patterns.

Estimating model quality

There are a number of tests that can be made to check the validity of the model. No one test is necessarily conclusive, but together they give a reasonable idea of quality.

Firstly, when examining the fit of models to single time series there are two principal tests based upon the autocorrelations of the residuals:

1. A check of autocorrelations against their confidence limit should result in no more than 1 in 20 outside the limit.
2. The Chi-Square parameter calculated from the autocorrelations should be less than the tabulated value.

Secondly, when examining the fit of the process model there are the following tests:

1. Plots of actual residuals against the input time series and against the output time series should show random scatters about means of zero with no apparent patterns.
2. A check of autocorrelations of the residuals against their confidence limit should result in no more than 1 in 20 outside the limit.
3. The Chi-Square parameter calculated from the autocorrelations should be less than the tabulated value.

4. A check of cross correlations of the residuals versus the input time series against their confidence limit should result in no more than 1 in 20 outside the limit.
5. The Chi-Square parameter calculated from the cross-correlations should be less than the tabulated value.
6. If an independent estimate of measurement error is available then an F-test can be made with the variance of the residuals.

If none of these tests are badly violated then there is a reasonable chance that the model is at least adequate.

3.6 Time series analysis on the evaporator

This section will use Time Series Analysis to develop a process model of the effect of the steam supply pressure $P100$ on the exit concentration $X2$.

An input time series was generated by adding to the normal steady-state value of $P100$ white noise with a standard deviation of 3.0 kPa and an $AR(3)$ filter with the denominator $1 - 1.97q^{-1} + 1.37q^{-2} - 0.34q^{-3}$. The nonlinear evaporator model then calculated an output $X2(t)$ to which more noise was added. This noise was generated using white noise with a standard deviation of 0.5 percent and an $AR(2)$ filter with the AR term $1 - 1.53q^{-1} + 0.63q^{-2}$. The separator level $L2$ and operating pressure $P2$ of the evaporator were controlled by two PI loops as discussed in Chapter 4. The data for this analysis is shown in Appendix C.

The data was then processed using the software package TSA (see Appendix A) following the procedure outlined above. The results will be discussed in the same order as the tests were:

1. The autocorrelations and partial autocorrelations for the input series are shown in Figures 3.6 and 3.7 respectively. The form of these indicated an $AR(3)$ model.

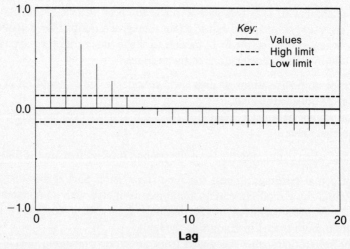

Figure 3.6 Input series autocorrelations

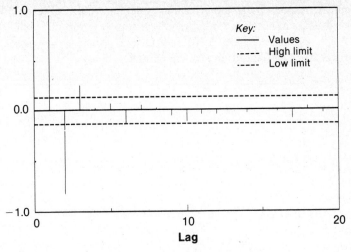

Figure 3.7 Input series partial autocorrelations

2. Nonlinear regression gave the AR term $1 - 1.93q^{-1} + 1.25q^{-2} - 0.25q^{-3}$ for the $AR(3)$ model with a Chi-square value of 5.5 with 10 degrees of freedom (less than the tabulated value of 18.3 at 95 percent confidence level and hence a significant degree of fit). There were no autocorrelations outside the confidence limits. This was in reasonable agreement with the filter used to generate the input time series. A plot of model prediction versus data is shown in Figure 3.8.

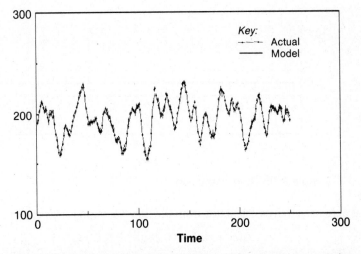

Figure 3.8 Model versus time series: Fit of input time series

3. The impulse response and step response are shown in Figures 3.9 and 3.10 respectively. Data in both figures indicate a process deadtime of 5 minutes. The form of the step response (Figure 3.10) indicates a second order model would be appropriate. An $ARMA(2, 0)$ model was chosen.

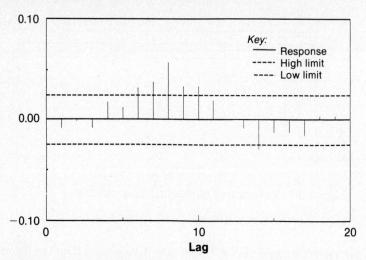

Figure 3.9 Impulse response

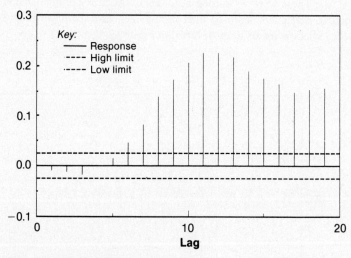

Figure 3.10 Step response

4. Initial parameter values calculated from the impulse response gave:

$$\Delta(q^{-1}) = 1 - 0.88q^{-1} + 0.018q^{-2}$$

and: $\qquad\qquad \Omega(q^{-1}) = 0.021$

5. The autocorrelations and partial autocorrelations for the residuals are shown in Figures 3.11 and 3.12 respectively. The form of these indicated an $AR(2)$ or $AR(3)$ model.

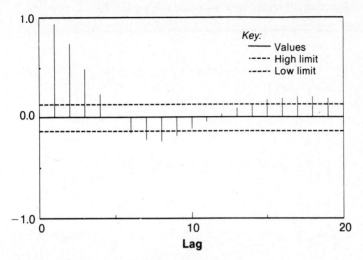

Figure 3.11 Residuals autocorrelations

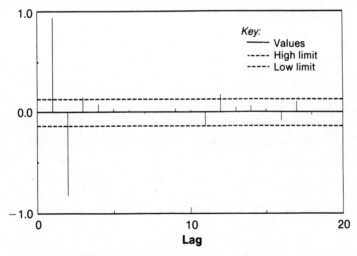

Figure 3.12 Residuals partial autocorrelations

6. Nonlinear regression gave a denominator for the $AR(2)$ model with a Chi-square value of 22 with 10 degrees of freedom (greater than the tabulated value of 18.3 at 95 percent confidence level). This was not a good fit. Nonlinear regression gave the denominator $1 - 1.84q^{-1} + 1.13q^{-2} - 0.17q^{-3}$ for the $AR(3)$ model with a Chi-square value of 14 with 10 degrees of freedom (less than the tabulated value of 18.3

at 95 percent confidence level and hence a reasonable fit). There was one autocorrelation outside the confidence limits. This is more complex than the filter used to generate the residuals. This is because it also includes modeling errors. A plot of model prediction versus data is shown in Figure 3.13.

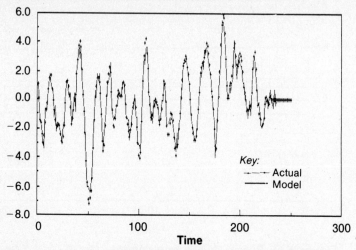

Figure 3.13 Model versus time series: Fit of residuals

7. The final nonlinear regression which fits the process and residual models gave the following process model:

$$(1 - 1.56q^{-1} + 0.74q^{-2})\, X2(t) = 0.0295\, P100(t - 5)$$

There was only one autocorrelation of the residuals outside the confidence limits (Figure 3.14) and the Chi-square value was 18.5 with 17 degrees of freedom (less than

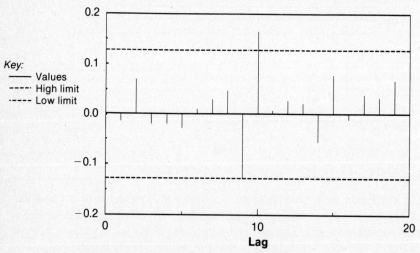

Figure 3.14 Autocorrelation of residuals

the tabulated value of 27.6 at 95 percent confidence level and hence a good fit). There were no cross correlations of the residuals versus the input outside the confidence limits (Figure 3.15) and the Chi-square value was 14.4 with 18 degrees of freedom. The residual plots (Figure 3.16 and 3.17) appeared randomly distributed about zero with no obvious patterns. All indications were that the model was a reasonable fit of the data (see Figure 3.18).

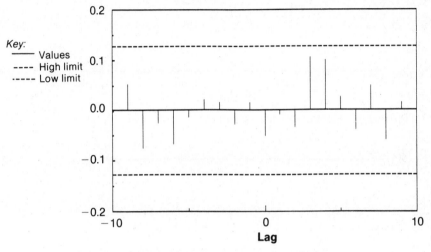

Figure 3.15 Residual input cross correlations

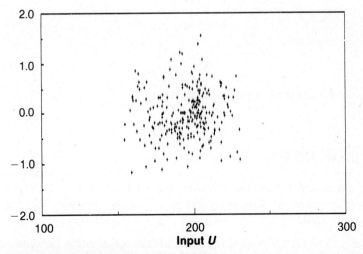

Figure 3.16 Residuals versus input

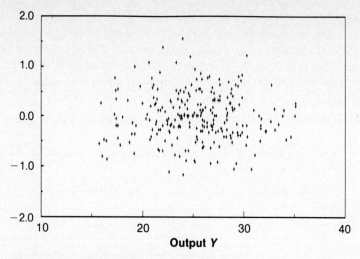

Figure 3.17 Residuals versus output

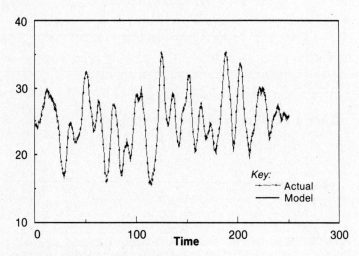

Figure 3.18 Final fit of model

3.7 Exercises

1. Perform a step test on the nonlinear evaporator model to determine a FOPDT model for the effect of feed composition $X1$ on the variable $X2$. Use the fitting technique of Smith.

2. Write a FORTRAN program to use a library optimization technique to refine the parameters determined in Exercise 1.

3.8 References

Astrom, K. J. and Wittenmark, B. (1984), *Computer Controlled Systems-Theory and Design*, Prentice Hall, Englewood Cliffs, NJ.

Box, G. E. P. and Jenkins, G. M. (1970), *Time Series Analysis, Forecasting and Control*, Holden Day, San Francisco.

Oldenbourg, R. C. and Sartorius, H. (1948), *The Dynamics of Automatic Control*, Trans ASME, p. 77.

Smith, C. L. (1972), *Digital Computer Process Control*, Intext Educational Publishers, Scranton, Pa.

4 Single loop control and the relative gain array

4.1 Introduction

For any process, the first approach to control is to install one or more single-input single-output control loops, generally using the ubiquitous proportional-integral-derivative control law.

In this chapter the following aspects of single-loop control will be examined: heuristic pairing of controlled and manipulated variables, tuning PID controller parameters, and measuring interactions using the Relative Gain Array.

4.2 Mass and energy inventory control

The application of heuristic control system design principles (see Appendix D) would lead, firstly, to a consideration of the process liquid and vapor mass balances.

The process liquid mass balance is:

$$\rho\, A\, dL2/dt \;=\; F1 \;-\; F4 \;-\; F2$$

which is not self-regulatory (since the state variable $L2$ does not appear on the right hand side of the equation) and hence *must* be controlled for stable operation. The guidelines for the selection of a manipulated variable lead to a pairing of $L2$ with $F2$, using a direct-acting stream leaving the process.

The process vapor mass balance is:

$$C\, dP2/dt \;=\; F4 \;-\; F5$$

which is self-regulatory and hence need *not* be controlled. That this variable is self-regulatory may not be readily apparent. If the pressure were to rise, so would the tube-side temperature and hence the heat transfer in the evaporator would decline. This in turn would slow the rate of vapor generation ($F4$) leading to the pressure stabilizing at a new constant value. The guidelines for the selection of a manipulated variable lead to a pairing of *P2* with *F200*, using indirect control (no direct control is possible) of a stream leaving the process which is also a utility stream.

The level and pressure controllers will maintain steady mass inventory control. The vapor inventory controller also controls the energy inventory since the system operates at its boiling point. Thus these two controllers maintain steady mass and energy inventory control.

4.3 Controller tuning

The liquid level control loop *L2–F2* is not self-regulatory and must be tuned by a closed loop technique. Applying the testing procedure of Ziegler and Nichols (1942) to the nonlinear model involves applying a setpoint change to a proportional-only controller and determining the gain of the controller at which the process first begins to oscillate with a constant amplitude. The result was:

$$K_u = 17.5 \text{ kg/min/m}$$
$$P_u = 8.2 \text{ min}$$

For a one-quarter decay ratio PI controller, Ziegler and Nichols recommend:

$$K_c = K_u/2.2 = 8.0 \text{ kg/min/m}$$
$$T_i = P_u/1.2 = 6.8 \text{ min}$$

The results for a setpoint change in level from 1.0 to 1.4 metres are shown in Figure 4.1. The controller gain was decreased and the integral time increased by 30 percent to give the response shown in Figure 4.2. The response now shows a damping ratio of approximately 0.2. The Ziegler and Nichols guidelines are strictly suited only to the types of processes on which they were developed, but generally provide a good first estimate.

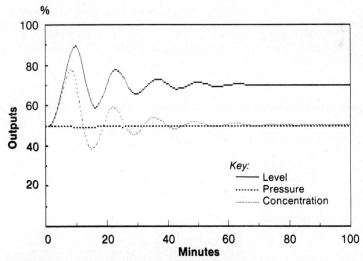

Figure 4.1 Ziegler–Nichols tuning of *L2* loop

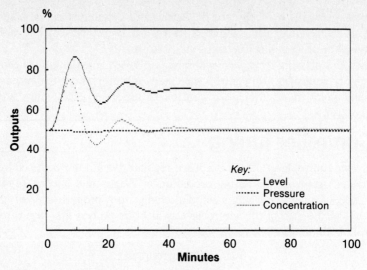

Figure 4.2 Modified tuning of *L2* loop

The pressure control loop *P2–F*200 is self-regulatory and can be tuned by a reaction curve technique (i.e. with the controller in manual-mode, a step change in the controller output is made and the response of the measurement is recorded). Twenty percent step changes in *F*200 resulted in the first-order plus deadtime (FOPDT) model parameters using the Fit 4 technique, explained in Smith and Corripio (1985) (see Table 4.1).

Table 4.1 *P2–F200 FOPDT model parameter estimates*

	20 percent increase	*20 percent decrease*
Gain (kPa/kg/min)	0.043	0.060
Time constant (min)	29.7	29.5
Deadtime (min)	1.3	0.5

These parameters demonstrate the nonlinearity of the system. Since the Ziegler and Nichols tuning formulae are invalid if the deadtime is less than one tenth the time constant, the following process parameters were used:

gain k = 0.051 kPa/(kg/min)
time constant τ = 29.6 min
deadtime T_d = 2.96 min

giving PI controller constants:

$$K_c = \frac{0.9\tau}{KT_d} = 176.5 \text{ kg/min/kPa}$$
$$T_i = 3.33T_d = 9.77 \text{ min}$$

The cooling water response with these constants for an increase in the setpoint of 0.5 kPa is shown in Figure 4.3. This response shows these constants give a conservative response with a small damping ratio.

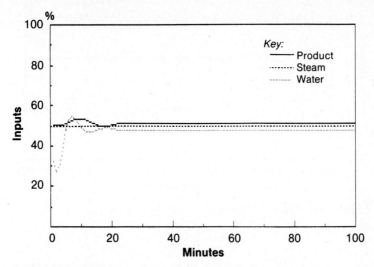

Figure 4.3 Reaction curve tuning of *P*2 loop

4.4 Product quality control

It is evident from Figures 4.1, 4.2 and 4.3 that the process is highly interactive, with product composition $X2$ responding vigorously to variations in the other variables. This would imply that attempts to control product quality by adjusting the steam pressure $P100$ may experience difficulties.

Step changes of plus 20 percent and minus 20 percent in $P100$ give oscillatory $X2$ responses and show steady state gains of 0.273 and 0.195 respectively. The nonlinearity of the process is again evident. The responses were unsuitable for reaction curve tuning, due to their oscillatory nature. As a result the Ziegler and Nichols (1942) testing procedure, as discussed in Section 4.3, was carried out on the nonlinear model, giving the results:

K_u = 3.6 kg/min/percent
P_u = 15 min

The corresponding Ziegler and Nichols recommended PI controller constants are:

K_c = 1.64 kg/min/percent
T_i = 12.5 min

which gave the results shown in Figure 4.4 for a decrease in setpoint from 25 percent to 18 percent. While stable, the approach to setpoint is very slow.

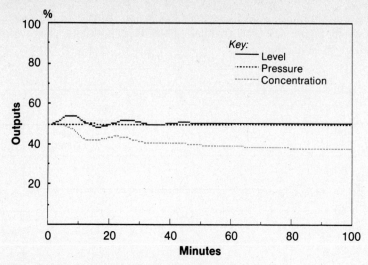

Figure 4.4 Ziegler–Nichols tuning of *X*2 loop

Reducing the integral time by a factor of four to 3.12 minutes gave the response in Figure 4.5.

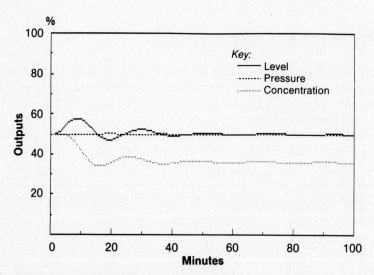

Figure 4.5 Increased *T*1 on *X*2 loop

It is evident from the product flowrate and cooling water responses in Figure 4.6 that interactions are strong.

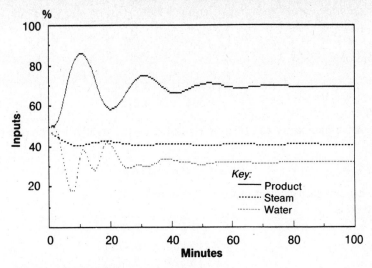

Figure 4.6 Multiloop interactions

4.5 Relative gain array

The strong interactions between $P2$ and $X2$ could have been predicted using Bristol's Relative Gain Array (RGA) (Bristol 1966).

In order to evaluate the RGA, steady state gains are required between $P2$, $X2$ and $F200$, $P100$. These can be determined from step tests, or more directly from the linear model.

Assume $dL2/dt = 0$ in the linear model:

$$d\underset{\sim}{x}/dt = \underset{\sim}{A}\underset{\sim}{x} + \underset{\sim}{B}\underset{\sim}{u}$$

derived in Chapter 2.

By eliminating $F2$ it follows that:

$$d\underset{\sim}{x_r}/dt = \underset{\sim}{A_r}\underset{\sim}{x_r} + \underset{\sim}{B_r}\underset{\sim}{u_r}$$

where: $\underset{\sim}{x_r}^T \doteq [X2 \ P2]$

$\quad\ \underset{\sim}{u_r}^T = [P100 \ F200]$

$$\underset{\sim}{A_r} = \begin{bmatrix} -0.20445 & -0.37935 \\ -0.01034 & -0.054738 \end{bmatrix}$$

$$\underset{\sim}{B_r} = \begin{bmatrix} 0.37266 & 0 \\ 0.036914 & -0.0075272 \end{bmatrix}$$

At steady state the process gains are determined from:

$$\underset{\sim}{x}_r = -\underset{\sim}{A}_r^{-1}\, \underset{\sim}{B}_r\, \underset{\sim}{u}_r = \underset{\sim}{K}\underset{\sim}{u}_r$$

giving gains of:

$$\underset{\sim}{K} = \begin{bmatrix} 0.880 & 0.393 \\ 0.508 & -0.212 \end{bmatrix}$$

The relative gain array can then be evaluated by the standard technique of Bristol (1966):

$$(RGA)_{ij} = ((K^{-1})^T)_{ij}(K)_{ij}$$

where $(\ )_{ij}$ denotes each element of the matrix in turn.

The result is:

$$RGA = \begin{array}{c} \\ X2 \\ P2 \end{array}\begin{array}{cc} P100 & F200 \\ \begin{bmatrix} 0.482 & 0.518 \\ 0.518 & 0.482 \end{bmatrix} \end{array}$$

An RGA element equal to unity indicates the desired pairing of output and manipulated variable with no interactions. The more an element deviates in value from unity, the stronger are the interactions. With all elements approximately 0.5, this indicates the strongest possible interactions. It also indicates that it may have been marginally better to pair the loops $X2$—$F200$ and $P2$—$P100$, although this would have been against "conventional wisdom".

4.6 Exercise

Reconfigure the single-loop controllers as suggested by the RGA analysis. Retune the loops using an appropriate method and compare and contrast the performance with Figures 4.5 and 4.6.

4.7 References

Bristol, E. H. (1966), "On a new measure of interaction for multivariable process control", *IEEE Trans Auto Control*, Vol. AC-11, No. 1, pp. 133-4.

Smith, C. A. and Corripio, A. B. (1985), *Principles and Practice of Automatic Process Control*, Wiley, New York.

Ziegler, J. G. and Nichols, N. B. (1942), Optimum Settings for Automatic Controllers, *Trans ASME*, Vol. 64, p. 759.

5 Feedforward control

5.1 Introduction

Feedforward control is the most common industrially applied sophistication to improve the performance of standard multiple single-input, single-output PID control systems.

The objective of feedforward control is to compensate for the effect of measured disturbances. It attempts to take control action with an effect equal and opposite to the effect of the disturbance. Ideally, the net effect on the process output of concern is zero (see Figure 5.1).

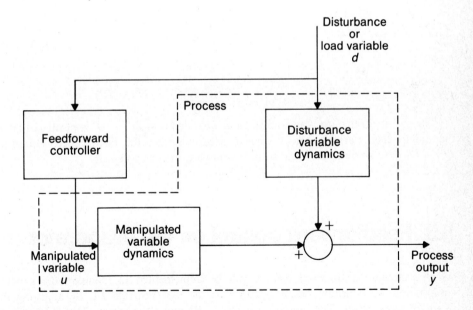

Figure 5.1 Feedforward control

5.2 Feedforward compensator design

In practice, two forms of compensator are used:

1. A single gain which makes a steady-state (static) compensation, but does not compensate dynamic effects.
2. A lead-lag compensator which partially takes into account dynamic effects.

In theory a perfect compensator may be realizable, but is seldom justifiable. The old adage, that the first 80 percent of the improvement can be obtained from the first 20 percent of the effort, generally applies to feedforward compensation.

The design procedure includes the following steps:

1. Select the disturbance variable d, the output variable y, and the manipulated variable u.
2. Obtain FOPDT models for the effect of the disturbance (between d and y) and for the effect of the manipulated variable (between u and y).
3. Design the compensator as discussed below.
4. Implement and test the compensator.

Identification techniques for obtaining the FOPDT models are described in Chapter 3. Suppose the models are:

$$y(kT_s) = \frac{b_0^d}{(1 + a_1^d q^{-1})} d(kT_s - D^d) + \frac{b_0^u}{(1 + a_1^u q^{-1})} u(kT_s - D^u)$$

The desired net effect is:

$$y(kT_s) = 0$$

Hence:

$$u(kT_s) = -\frac{b_0^d(1 + a_1^u q^{-1})}{b_0^u(1 + a_1^d q^{-1})} d(kT_s - D^d + D^u)$$

This is a realizable lead-lag compensator provided that $D^d - D^u$ is positive, that is, the manipulated variable has a smaller deadtime than the disturbance. Otherwise $D^d - D^u$ must be set to zero and some loss in performance accepted.

5.3 Feedforward control on the evaporator

As an example, feedforward control will be implemented to maintain the product composition $X2$ constant, despite changes in the feed flowrate $F1$, by adjusting the steam pressure $P100$. The operating pressure $P2$ and the separator level $L2$ will be controlled by PI feedback controllers (see Chapter 4).

Using the step test technique described in Chapter 3, an FOPDT model for $F1$–$X2$ was identified as:

gain $\quad\quad\quad$ = $-4.65\%/(\text{kg}/\text{min})$
time constant = 3.9 min
deadtime $\quad\quad$ = 4.0 min

Hence, in discrete terms for a sample time of 1 minute:

$$X2(k) = -0.939(1 - 0.796q^{-1})^{-1} F1(k - 4)$$

A similar exercise identified a FOPDT model for $P100$–$X2$ as:

gain $\quad\quad\quad$ = 0.24% kPa
time constant = 5.4 min
deadtime $\quad\quad$ = 4.0 min

and in discrete terms:

$$X2(k) = 0.0375(1 - 0.844q^{-1})^{-1} P100(k - 4)$$

The resulting discrete lead-lag compensator is:

$$P100(k) = 25.0 \frac{(1 - 0.844q^{-1})}{(1 - 0.796q^{-1})} F1(k)$$

or if the dynamics are ignored the static compensator is:

$$P100(k) = 19.12\ F1(k)$$

A number of simulations were performed for a 10 percent decrease in feed flowrate $F1$ and can be compared visually in Figures 5.2, 5.3 and 5.4 and by examining the integral of the squared error over 100 minutes as shown in Table 5.1.

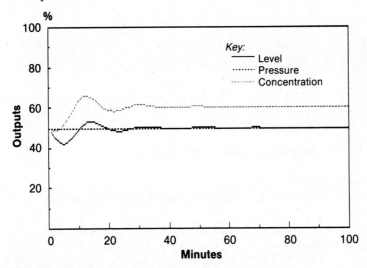

Figure 5.2 Open-loop response

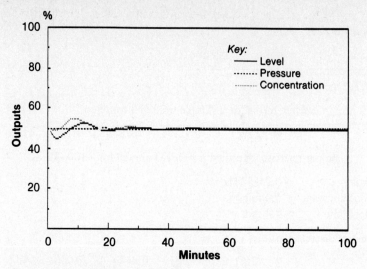

Figure 5.3 Static feedforward

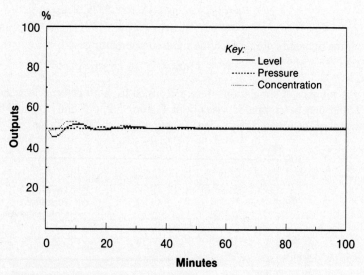

Figure 5.4 Dynamic feedforward

Table 5.1 *Comparison of control strategy performance*

	Figure	ISE
Open loop	5.2	2662.6
Static feedforward	5.3	32.9
Dynamic feedforward	5.4	16.3

Note that, because the time constants of the disturbance effect (1.8 min) and of the manipulated variable effect (2.3 min) were close, static feedforward performed almost as well as dynamic feedforward.

Dynamic feedforward was also tested for a variety of step sizes for the disturbance in $F1$ (see Table 5.2).

Table 5.2 *Dynamic feedforward performance*

Step size	ISE
20 percent decrease	89.7
15 percent decrease	42.6
10 percent decrease	16.3
5 percent decrease	3.5
0 percent change	0.0
5 percent increase	3.3
10 percent increase	16.4
15 percent increase	284.2
20 percent increase	880.9

Comparing 5 and 10 percent changes in both directions, there is a small difference due to the nonlinearity of the actual process gain (the FOPDT models used in the feedforward controller were derived from the responses to 5 percent increases and decreases in $F1$ and $P100$). For larger decreases, the pressure control loop became unstable because of increased process gain at these operating conditions. For larger increases, the cooling water flowrate $F200$ saturated and pressure control was lost completely.

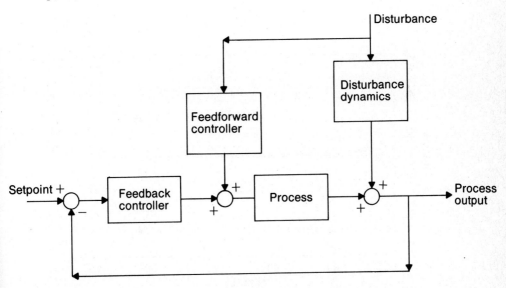

Figure 5.5 Combined feedforward and feedback control structure

The results above indicate the weakness of feedforward control. As it is model-based, it will only be effective when the model is an accurate representation of the process behavior. In practice, feedforward control is nearly always used in conjunction with feedback control. Feedback control will compensate for any modeling errors and ensure that the process is returned to setpoint.

Combined feedforward-feedback control was implemented, as shown in Figure 5.5. Both the feedback and feedforward controllers contribute in determining the value of the manipulated variable.

Further simulation runs for a 10 percent decrease in $F1$ were performed as shown in Table 5.3.

Table 5.3 *Comparison of control strategy performance*

	Figure	ISE
Feedforward only	5.4	16.3
Feedforward/Feedback	5.6	22.8
Feedback only	5.7	428.0

The strong interactions between the pressure control loop ($P2 - F200$) and the composition control loop destabilized control marginally (compare Figures 5.4 and 5.6) when feedback was added. However it can also be seen that the feedforward control greatly improved the performance of the feedback control for disturbances in $F1$ (compare Figures 5.6 and 5.7).

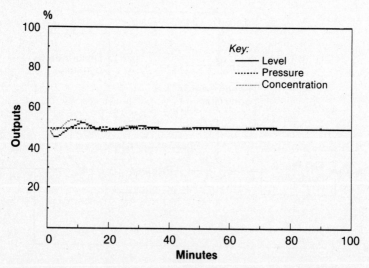

Figure 5.6 Combined dynamic feedforward and feedback

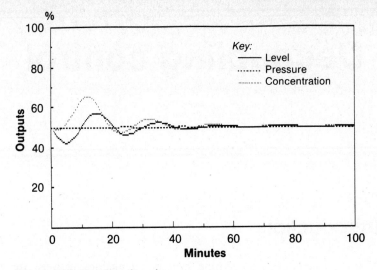

Figure 5.7 Feedback only

5.4 Exercise

Design, implement and test feedforward compensation for the effect of $X1$ on $X2$ using $P100$ as the manipulated variable.

6 Decoupling control

6.1 Introduction

The poor control resulting from strong process interactions between the pressure control loop and the composition control loop on the evaporator has been previously noted in Chapters 4 and 5. This is quite a common problem in single-input, single-output control systems. The interactions between loops attempting to control both top and bottom compositions on distillation columns is another infamous example of a common problem.

Chapter 5 examined feedforward control where compensators are used to reduce the effects of a measured disturbance. It is natural to ask whether such compensators could be used to reduce the effects of another control loop. The answer, of course, is yes. Compensators which reduce the effects of other manipulated variables on a control loop are called decouplers or decoupling compensators or, simply, decoupling control.

6.2 Decoupling compensator design

The design process is analogous to the design of feedforward compensators, although the structure is a little more complex (see Figure 6.1). Consider the decoupling of two control loops; the procedure can be readily extended to more loops. The design steps are:

1. Determine the output variables y_1 and y_2 and the corresponding manipulated variables u_1 and u_2. In this case there are no disturbance variables; u_2 is the "disturbance" to $u_1 - y_1$ and u_1 is the "disturbance" to $u_2 - y_2$.
2. Obtain FOPDT models for the effects of u_1 on y_1 and y_2 and of u_2 on y_1 and y_2. More complex models can be used.
3. Design the compensators as described below.
4. Implement and test the decoupler, preferably open loop and then closed loop.

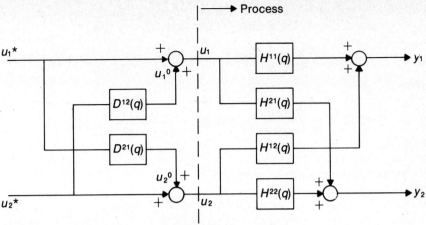

* The calculated inputs from appropriate feedback controllers.

Figure 6.1 Decoupler structure

Assuming FOPDT models were used, the first compensator is designed as follows:

The model for the effect of u_1 and u_2 on y_1 would be:

$$y_1(kT_s) = \frac{b_0^{11}}{(1 + a_1^{11}q^{-1})} u_1(kT_s - D^{11}) + \frac{b_0^{12}}{(1 + a_1^{12}q^{-1})} u_2(kT_s - D^{12})$$

The objective of this compensator is to adjust u_1 such that y_1 is unaffected by u_2, hence the compensator is:

$$u_1^0(kT_s) = -\frac{b_0^{12}(1 + a_1^{11}q^{-1})}{b_0^{11}(1 + a_1^{12}q^{-1})} u_2^*(kT_s - D^{12} + D^{11})$$

As for feedforward compensators, conditions of realizability apply for the deadtime $D^{12} - D^{11}$ (see Chapter 5).

The second compensator is designed in a similar fashion giving:

$$u_2^0(kT_s) = -\frac{b_0^{21}(1 + a_1^{22}q^{-1})}{b_0^{22}(1 + a_1^{21}q^{-1})} u_1^*(kT_s - D^{21} + D^{22})$$

The connection equations for the decoupler summers (see Figure 6.1) are:

$$u_i(kT_s) = u_i^*(kT_s) + u_i^0(kT_s)$$

for $i = 1, 2$.

6.3 Decoupler design for the evaporator

Consider a 2×2 decoupler which attempts to reduce the interactions between the operating pressure control loop *P2–F200* and the product composition control loop

X2–P100. Step tests were performed with the P2 and X2 control loops open, but the L2 loop remaining closed. The resulting FOPDT models are:

$$X2(k) = \frac{0.00170}{(1 - 0.960q^{-1})} F200(k - 7) + \frac{0.0393}{(1 - 0.706q^{-1})} P100(k - 4)$$

and:

$$P2(k) = \frac{0.00504}{(1 - 0.960q^{-1})} P100(k) + \frac{0.001535}{(1 - 0.970q^{-1})} F200(k)$$

The corresponding compensators are therefore:

$$P100^0(k) = -0.04326 \frac{(1 - 0.706q^{-1})}{(1 - 0.960q^{-1})} F200^*(k - 3)$$

and:

$$F200^0(k) = 3.283 \frac{(1 - 0.970q^{-1})}{(1 - 0.960q^{-1})} P100^*(k)$$

These compensators were implemented by simulation on the nonlinear model.

The evaporator was first tested without decouplers. The X2–P100* PI control loops used the same controller constants determined in Chapter 4. Figures 6.2 and 6.3 show the responses to step changes in the disturbance variable F1 of 15 percent and 100 percent in X1 respectively.

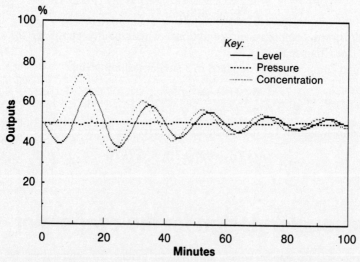

Figure 6.2 Response without decouplers to F1 decrease

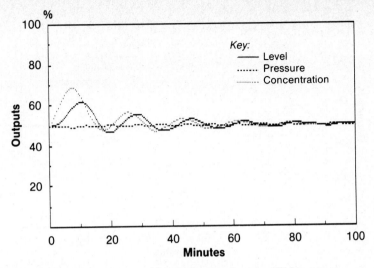

Figure 6.3 Response without decouplers to $X1$ increase

The decoupler results are shown in Figures 6.4 and 6.5 for the same step disturbances of 15 percent in $F1$ and of 100 percent in $X1$ respectively. Visual examination shows a marked improvement in the stability of the system although little decrease in the initial deviations. The problems with the decouplers designed above are:

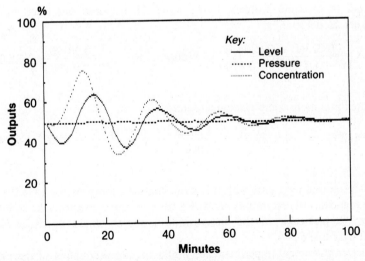

Figure 6.4 First-order decouplers to $F1$ decrease

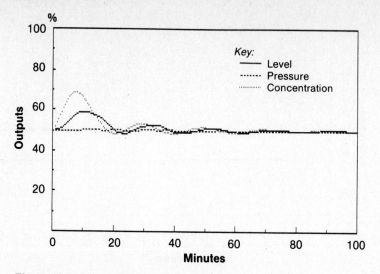

Figure 6.5 First-order decouplers to $X1$ increase

1. The $X2$–$P100$ step response was an oscillatory response not well represented by a FOPDT model.
2. There is an interaction between this loop and the level loop which was not considered.

In order to examine problem 1, the $X2$–$P100$ response was fitted by a general second order model giving:

$$X2(k) = \frac{0.023(1 + 0.024q^{-1})}{(1 - 1.713q^{-1} + 0.870q^{-2})} P100(k - 6) + \frac{0.00170}{(1 - 0.960q^{-1})} F200(k - 7)$$

This resulted in a more complex compensator:

$$P100^0(k) = -0.0739 \frac{(1 - 1.713q^{-1} + 0.870q^{-2})}{(1 - 0.960q^{-1})(1 + 0.024q^{-1})} - F200^*(k - 1)$$

The same closed loop tests with this more complex compensator gave the results in Figures 6.6 and 6.7. These results showed a further improvement in the stability of the two loops, in particular of the composition loop, as would be expected. This is confirmed by Table 6.1.

Further improvement in performance would require decoupling of the interactions with the $L2$–$F2$ control loop which are clearly demonstrated in all the responses.

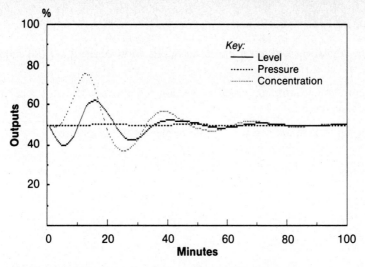

Figure 6.6 Mixed-order decouplers to *F*1 decrease

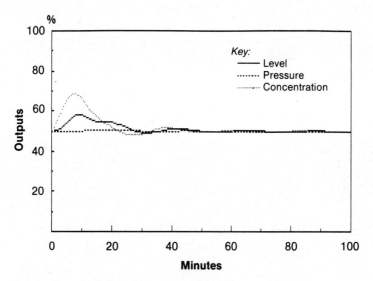

Figure 6.7 Mixed-order decouplers to *X*1 increase

Table 6.1 Decay ratio values

	*F*1 + 15%	*X*1 + 100%
no decoupler	0.44	0.32
simple decoupler	0.36	0.18
complex decoupler	0.25	0.05

6.4 Exercises

1. Design, implement and test a 2 × 2 decoupler between the $X2$–$P100$ control loop and the $L2$–$F2$ control loop.

2. Combine the decoupler discussed in Section 6.3 above with the 2 × 2 decoupler designed in Exercise 6.1.

3. Design, implement and test a 3 × 3 decoupler for the evaporator.

7 The linear multivariable regulator

7.1 Introduction

The decoupling control presented in Chapter 6 adds compensators to attempt to remove process interactions between single-input, single-output control loops.

A possibly better alternative is to attempt to use the interactions by implementing a true multi-input, multi-output controller. The linear multivariable regulator (LMR) is one such controller. As will be seen, the disadvantage of the LMR is that a reasonable linear state space model of the process is required. The development of such a model may be expensive, however very poor control of an interacting process is also costly.

7.2 LMR design

Much of the work in this chapter is derived from earlier research by one of the authors (Newell and Fisher 1972). Firstly the design process requires a discrete-time, linear state-space model (preferably in normalized perturbation variables) of the process of the form:

$$\underset{\sim}{x}_{k+1} = \underset{\sim}{\Phi}\underset{\sim}{x}_k + \underset{\sim}{\Delta}\underset{\sim}{u}_k$$

and secondly an objective function that the design process attempts to minimize:

$$J = \sum_i (\underset{\sim}{x}_i^T \underset{\sim}{Q} \underset{\sim}{x}_i + \underset{\sim}{u}_i^T \underset{\sim}{R} \underset{\sim}{u}_i)$$

where: $\underset{\sim}{Q}$ and $\underset{\sim}{R}$ are diagonal matrices with positive diagonal elements.

The q_{ii} elements apply a weighting or cost, to deviations from setpoint of the states.

The r_{ii} elements apply a weighting or penalty to the use of a manipulated variable.

53

It is simple to relate these elements to a quadratic cost index for deviations from setpoint of an operating condition, or for the use of a control action. The usual design procedure is to solve a form of the matrix Ricatti equation:

$$\underset{\sim}{P}_{k+1} = \underset{\sim}{\Phi}^T \underset{\sim}{P}_k \underset{\sim}{\Phi} - \underset{\sim}{\Phi}^T \underset{\sim}{P}_k \underset{\sim}{\Delta} (\underset{\sim}{\Delta}^T \underset{\sim}{P}_k \underset{\sim}{\Delta} + \underset{\sim}{R})^{-1} \underset{\sim}{\Delta}^T \underset{\sim}{P}_k \underset{\sim}{\Phi} + \underset{\sim}{Q}$$

for $\underset{\sim}{P}_\infty$ where: $\underset{\sim}{P}_0 = \underset{\sim}{I}$.

In practice the value of $\underset{\sim}{P}$ becomes approximately constant (to four decimal places) after 40 to 100 iterations.

The controller gain matrix, defined by the relation:

$$\underset{\sim}{u}_k = \underset{\sim}{K}_c \underset{\sim}{x}_k$$

is computed from the relation:

$$\underset{\sim}{K}_c = -(\underset{\sim}{\Delta}^T \underset{\sim}{P} \underset{\sim}{\Delta} + \underset{\sim}{R})^{-1} \underset{\sim}{\Delta}^T \underset{\sim}{P} \underset{\sim}{\Phi}$$

Computer programs exist to both generate a discrete-time version of the state-space model from a given continuous time state-space model, and to solve the above matrix Ricatti equation (see Appendix A).

Two things should be noted about the control law:

1. All the process states must be measured or estimated in some way (see Chapter 8).
2. The controller is simply a multivariable proportional controller which will suffer from the problem of offset.

Offset with the LMR can often be ignored, since the controller gains are generally effectively much higher than those of single-input, single-output controllers so that the offsets are correspondingly smaller. If this is not possible, then the LMR design problem can be formulated to produce integral action as well, by introducing so-called integral states:

$$\underset{\sim}{z} = \int \underset{\sim}{x} \, dt$$

or:

$$d\underset{\sim}{z}/dt = \underset{\sim}{x}$$

and augmenting the state equation:

$$\frac{d}{dt}\begin{bmatrix} \underset{\sim}{x} \\ \underset{\sim}{z} \end{bmatrix} = \begin{bmatrix} \underset{\sim}{A} & \underset{\sim}{0} \\ \underset{\sim}{I} & \underset{\sim}{0} \end{bmatrix} \begin{bmatrix} \underset{\sim}{x} \\ \underset{\sim}{z} \end{bmatrix} + \begin{bmatrix} \underset{\sim}{B} \\ \underset{\sim}{0} \end{bmatrix} \underset{\sim}{u}$$

then using the same design equations with the augmented matrices substituted.

The resulting control law is:

$$\underset{\sim}{u} = [\underset{\sim}{K}_c \ \underset{\sim}{K}_I] \begin{bmatrix} \underset{\sim}{x} \\ \underset{\sim}{z} \end{bmatrix} = \underset{\sim}{K}_c \underset{\sim}{x} + \underset{\sim}{K}_I \int \underset{\sim}{x} \, dt$$

Two points should be made about this augmented proportional plus integral LMR:

1. There cannot be more integral states than there are manipulated variables, by simple

degrees of freedom analysis. If the number of states exceeds the number of manipulated variables, then I in the augmented state-matrix is replaced by an arbitrary matrix V, which simply selects those states for which integral action or integral states are required.

2. In implementing the integral form, it is generally found necessary to weight the integral states in the augmented Q weighting matrix an order of magnitude less than the states themselves. This generally ensures stability.

7.3 LMR control of the evaporator

A two dimensional LMR was designed, based upon the reduced state space model:

$$\frac{d}{dt}\begin{bmatrix} X2 \\ P2 \end{bmatrix} = \begin{bmatrix} -0.20445 & -0.37935 \\ -0.01034 & -0.05474 \end{bmatrix}\begin{bmatrix} X2 \\ P2 \end{bmatrix} + \begin{bmatrix} 0.37266 & 0.0 \\ 0.03691 & -0.007527 \end{bmatrix}\begin{bmatrix} P100 \\ F200 \end{bmatrix}$$

This LMR is based upon the assumption that the separator level is maintained constant by a PI loop control, as discussed in Chapters 2, 3 and 4.

The LMR was to be compared with PI control in Chapter 4 and the 2×2 decoupler in Chapter 6. However, when implemented on the nonlinear model derived in Chapter 2, the system proved to be unstable for a 15 percent decrease in feed flowrate. This was due to the strong process interactions between the separator level control loop and the $P2$–$X2$ multivariable controller.

This instability demonstrates that when implementing multivariable control systems, they should encompass all the states which significantly interact with each other even when, as in this case, the interaction is via the PI loop and $X2$.

A three dimensional LMR was then designed, based upon the state-space model derived in Chapter 2 encompassing:

$$x^T = [L2 \quad X2 \quad P2]$$
$$u^T = [F2 \quad P100 \quad F200]$$

With all states and manipulated variables equally weighted, the control law was:

$$u = \begin{bmatrix} 0.28 & 0.42 & 0.57 \\ 0.79 & 0.098 & 0.70 \\ 0.043 & -0.002 & 0.32 \end{bmatrix} x$$

The performance of this 3×3 LMR is shown in Figure 7.1 for a 15 percent decrease in feed flowrate and was remarkably stable compared to the PI loops, even when decoupled (refer to Figure 6.6). As expected with proportional control there are offsets particularly noticeable in $P2$ and $L2$.

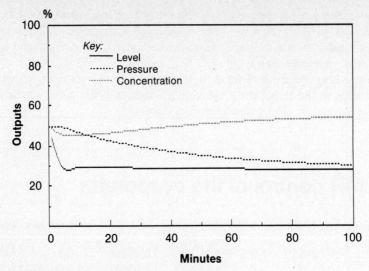

Figure 7.1 Multivariable control (1:1:1)

In Figure 7.2, again for a 15 percent decrease in feed flowrate, state weightings of 10, 1, 100 were used in place of the equal weightings 1, 1, 1 of Figure 7.1 ($\underset{\sim}{R}$ was held constant at diag(1, 1, 1). The control law was:

$$\underset{\sim}{u} = \begin{bmatrix} 0.94 & 0.34 & 5.17 \\ 1.52 & 0.16 & -1.77 \\ 0.49 & -0.10 & 5.33 \end{bmatrix} \underset{\sim}{x}$$

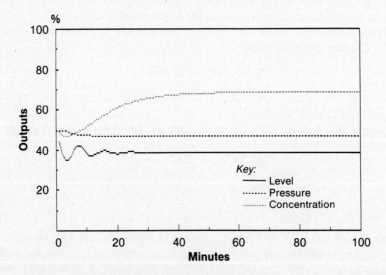

Figure 7.2 Multivariable control (10:1:100)

As expected the offsets in *L*2 and *P*2 were decreased but at the expense of an increased offset in *X*2. Since the weightings are all relative figures it becomes a matter of trade-offs to arrive at the "best" values.

Finally a proportional plus integral LMR was designed with the weightings 1, 1, 1 on the states *L*2, *X*2, *P*2 and weightings of 0.1, 0.1, 0.1 on their integrals. Less weighting on the integrals is generally required for stability. The control law is:

$$
\underset{\sim}{u} = \begin{bmatrix} 0.35 & 1.70 & 0.85 \\ 0.23 & -0.25 & 0.71 \\ 0.70 & -0.63 & 6.95 \end{bmatrix} \underset{\sim}{x} + \begin{bmatrix} 0.060 & 0.27 & 0.059 \\ 0.23 & -0.076 & -0.034 \\ 0.019 & -0.072 & 0.30 \end{bmatrix} \int \underset{\sim}{x}\, dt
$$

giving the results shown in Figure 7.3 for a 15 percent decrease in the feed flowrate. As expected the offsets are removed giving much improved control performance.

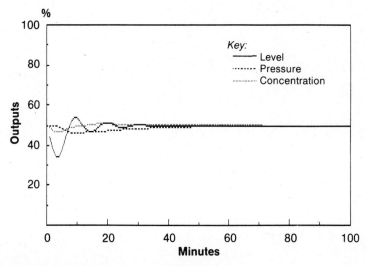

Figure 7.3 Multivariable PI control (1:1:1)

7.4 Exercises

1. Investigate the effects of varying the manipulated variable weightings upon offsets for a proportional LMR applied to the nonlinear evaporator model.

2. Select an "optimal" set of state weightings which apply tight control to product composition, reasonable control of operating pressure and which simply keep separator level within bounds (±0.7 metre). Use a proportional LMR on the nonlinear evaporator model. Use various feed condition disturbances.

3. Investigate the effect of integral state weighting relative to state weighting upon the stability of a PI LMR applied to the nonlinear evaporator model. Use some appropriate measures of relative stability.

7.5 References

Newell, R. B. and Fisher, D. G. (1972), "Experimental evaluation of optimal, multivariable regulatory controllers with model-following capabilities", *Automatica*, Vol. 8, pp. 247–62.

8 State estimation

8.1 Introduction

In many process environments, it is often not possible to measure all the state variables. Even if it is possible to measure some or all of the state variables, these measurements are often contaminated with a noise component. State estimation is a means of either:

1. estimating the complete state vector from a set of incomplete measurements; and/or
2. filtering noisy measurements to obtain the best estimates of the state variables.

   One of the most common methods used for state estimation is the Kalman filter. Sections 8.4 and 8.5 of this chapter will concentrate on the theory of the Kalman filter and its application to the evaporator problem.

8.2 Observability

An important property of a system which must be considered is observability. Observability of a system implies that, given a set of outputs or "measurements", it is possible to reconstruct the state vector. Obviously this property of a system is essential before any state estimation scheme is implemented.

   Observability tests are generally available for linear systems. Given a state-space linear model of the form:

$$\frac{d\underset{\sim}{x}}{dt} = \underset{\sim}{A}\underset{\sim}{x} + \underset{\sim}{B}\underset{\sim}{u} \qquad (8.1)$$

$$\underset{\sim}{y} = \underset{\sim}{C}\underset{\sim}{x} \qquad (8.2)$$

where: $\underset{\sim}{x}$ is the vector of n states.

$\underset{\sim}{y}$ is the vector of outputs.

$\underset{\sim}{u}$ is the vector of control variables.

$\underset{\sim}{A}$, $\underset{\sim}{B}$ and $\underset{\sim}{C}$ are constant real matrices.

59

Then the system is observable if:

$$W = [C^T \mid A^T \, C^T \mid (A^2)^T \, C^T \mid \dots \, (A^{n-1})^T \, C^T] \qquad (8.3)$$

has the same rank as there are states, that is, n.

A FORTRAN program to perform this test is available (see Appendix A).

8.3 Observability of the evaporator

For the linear evaporator model, defined in Chapter 2, the matrices A and B were given by:

$$A = \begin{bmatrix} 0 & 0.10445 & 0.37935 \\ 1 & -0.1 & 0 \\ 0 & -0.10340 \times 10^{-1} & -0.54738 \times 10^{-1} \end{bmatrix} \qquad (8.4)$$

$$B = \begin{bmatrix} -0.1 & -0.37266 & 0 \\ -0.1 & 0 & 0 \\ 0 & 0.36914 \times 10^{-1} & -0.75272 \times 10^{-2} \end{bmatrix} \qquad (8.5)$$

where: $x^T = [L2 \quad X2 \quad P2]$ $\qquad (8.6)$

$u^T = [F2 \quad P100 \quad F200]$ $\qquad (8.7)$

If we assume that both $L2$ and $P2$ are measurable, but we are unable to measure the exit concentration $X2$, then the C matrix is given as:

$$C = \begin{bmatrix} 1 & 0 & 0 \\ 0 & 0 & 1 \end{bmatrix} \qquad (8.8)$$

and

$$y^T = [L2 \quad P2] \qquad (8.9)$$

Using this information the rank of W (Equation 8.3) is three and the system is observable. This implies that the unmeasured state variable, exit concentration, can be estimated.

8.4 Kalman filter

A Kalman filter is one method of performing state estimation. A linear state-space model of the process is represented as:

$$\frac{dx}{dt} = Ax + Bu + Dd + w \qquad (8.10)$$

$$y = Cx + v \qquad (8.11)$$

or its discrete-time equivalent:

$$\underset{\sim}{x}(k + 1) = \underset{\sim}{\Phi}\underset{\sim}{x}(k) + \underset{\sim}{\Delta}\underset{\sim}{u}(k) + \underset{\sim}{\Theta}\underset{\sim}{d}(k) + \underset{\sim}{w} \qquad (8.12)$$

$$\underset{\sim}{y}(k) = \underset{\sim}{C}\underset{\sim}{x}(k) + \underset{\sim}{v} \qquad (8.13)$$

where $\underset{\sim}{w}$ and $\underset{\sim}{v}$ represent noise vectors.

This model is shown in Figure 8.1.

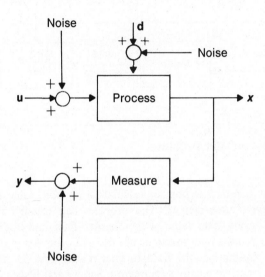

Figure 8.1 System structure

Given this model, then the Kalman filter algorithm is:

1. Prediction:

$$\underset{\sim}{\bar{x}}(k + 1) = \underset{\sim}{\Phi}\underset{\sim}{\hat{x}}(k) + \underset{\sim}{\Delta}\underset{\sim}{u}(k) + \underset{\sim}{\Theta}\underset{\sim}{d}(k) \qquad (8.14)$$

2. Correction:

$$\underset{\sim}{\hat{x}}(k) = \underset{\sim}{\bar{x}}(k) + \underset{\sim}{K}(k)\,[\underset{\sim}{y}(k) - \underset{\sim}{C}\underset{\sim}{\bar{x}}(k)] \qquad (8.15)$$

where $\underset{\sim}{K}(k)$ is the Kalman filter matrix at time k.

This structure is shown in Figure 8.2.

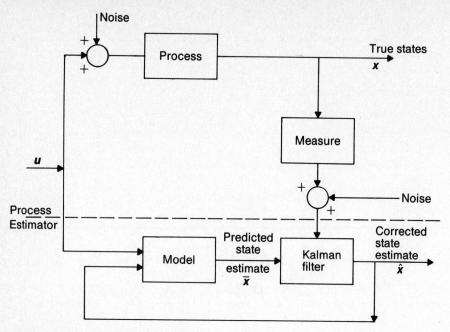

Figure 8.2 Kalman filter structure

The obvious question is how to calculate a suitable value for the Kalman filter matrix $\underset{\sim}{K}$ at every time step k. The problem can usually be simplified by only considering the steady state value of the Kalman filter matrix. This approximation is reasonable if the process time constants are small in comparison to the observation time NT_s. With this assumption, the Kalman filter matrix may be obtained by solving the following set of recursive relations (Hamilton, Seborg and Fisher 1973):

$$\underset{\sim}{K}(k) = \underset{\sim}{P}(k) \, \underset{\sim}{C}^T \, \underset{\sim}{R}^{-1} \tag{8.16}$$

$$\underset{\sim}{M}(k + 1) = \underset{\sim}{\Phi}\underset{\sim}{P}(k)\underset{\sim}{\Phi}^T + \underset{\sim}{\Gamma}\underset{\sim}{Q}\underset{\sim}{\Gamma}^T \tag{8.17}$$

$$\underset{\sim}{P}(k) = (\underset{\sim}{I} - \underset{\sim}{K}(k) \, \underset{\sim}{C})\underset{\sim}{M}(k) \tag{8.18}$$

where: Q is the covariance matrix of the process noise.
$\tilde{R}$ is the covariance matrix of the measurement noise.
$\underset{\sim}{\Gamma} = [\underset{\sim}{\Delta} \mid \underset{\sim}{\Theta}]$.

and the assumed initial conditions:

$$\underset{\sim}{M}(0) = \underset{\sim}{P}(0) = E\{[\underset{\sim}{x}(0) - \hat{\underset{\sim}{x}}(0)][\underset{\sim}{x}(0) - \hat{\underset{\sim}{x}}(0)]^T\} \tag{8.19}$$

Generally, the value of the expectation operator is zero. Starting with these initial conditions, the set of recursive relations are solved to their steady-state solutions for a constant value of $\underset{\sim}{K}$. A FORTRAN program to perform these calculations is available (Appendix A).

The Q and R matrices may be used as design variables. Generally $Q = qI$ and $R = rI$ and it is the ratio of q/r that becomes important. If q/r is low, then more emphasis is placed on the model prediction. If q/r is high, then more emphasis is placed on the actual plant measurements.

A simple algorithm to implement a Kalman filter is:

1. Collect noisy measurements.
2. Evaluate predicted state estimates from the model.
3. Correct state estimates with the Kalman filter.
4. Store changes in input variables (control and disturbance variables) for next sample time.
5. Wait sample time.
6. Go to step 1.

8.5 Application to the evaporator

Application of a Kalman filter to the evaporator system described in Chapter 2 required the addition of both process and measurement noise signals as shown in Figure 8.1. Gaussian noise of variance 0.1 was added to the process variables while Gaussian noise of variance 0.1 was added to the level measurement and variance 5.0 was added to the pressure measurement. This resulted in the following design matrices:

$$Q = \text{diag} [0.1 \quad 0.1 \quad 0.1 \quad 0.1 \quad 0.1 \quad 0.1 \quad 0.1 \quad 0.1]$$

$$R = \text{diag} [0.1 \quad 5.0]$$

The Kalman filter was implemented in conjunction with the PI control strategy described in Chapter 4. However, with the addition of the noise signals, new tuning constants were required. The constants used were:

$$L2–F2 \text{ loop} \qquad K_c = 3.0, \quad T_I = 9.1$$

$$P2–F200 \text{ loop} \qquad K_c = 10.0, \quad T_I = 9.0$$

$$X2–P100 \text{ loop} \qquad K_c = 0.10, \quad T_I = 3.12$$

With these values and a sample time of 1.0 minute, the Kalman filter design program (refer Appendix A) was used to obtain a steady state Kalman filter matrix K:

$$K = \begin{bmatrix} 0.476 \times 10^{-1} & -0.369 \times 10^{-5} \\ 0.605 \times 10^{-1} & 0.184 \times 10^{-5} \\ -0.185 \times 10^{-1} & 0.404 \times 10^{-5} \end{bmatrix}$$

The results of applying the Kalman filter to the evaporator for state estimation are shown in Figures 8.3, 8.4 and 8.5. These plots show for each state variable the true state value, the value measured by a transducer of the same noise variance as described (if such a transducer were available), and the estimated state variable. These responses were obtained for a feed flowrate disturbance from 10.0 kg/min down to 8.5 kg/min. It can be seen that for each variable the state estimate closely follows the true state value. For those state variables that could be measured—pressure and level (Figures 8.3 and 8.4)—the Kalman filter acts as a very good noise filter of the process measurements. For the state variable that could not be measured—exit concentration (Figure 8.5)—the Kalman filter provides an excellent estimate of the state variable.

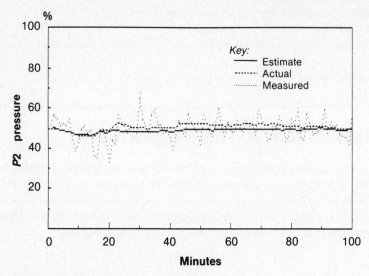

Figure 8.3 Estimation of pressure

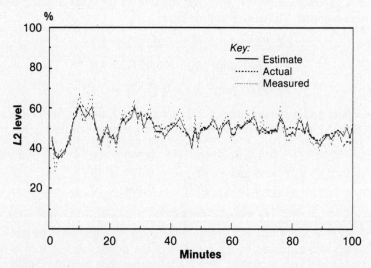

Figure 8.4 Estimation of level

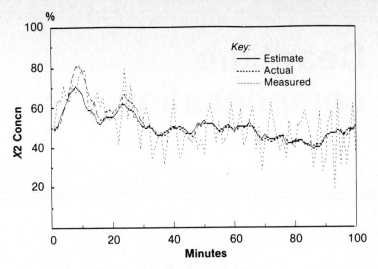

Figure 8.5 Estimation of exit concentration

8.6 Exercises

1. For the evaporator system, determine the minimum number of measurements and which variables to measure, to still enable state estimation of all the states to occur.

The following exercises will explore the behavior of the Kalman filter.

2. The responses shown in Figures 8.3, 8.4 and 8.5 were all obtained with estimation values set equal to the correct initial values. Examine the effects of incorrect initial values in the estimation process.

3. Examine the effect of varying the design estimates of the process and measurement noise variances, while retaining constant values of these variables in the implementation.

4. Use the estimated value of the exit concentration as the measured value in the $X2$–$P100$ control loop and compare the controlled response with that obtained from using the true value.

5. Set one column of the disturbance matrix D equal to zero. Redesign the Kalman filter on this basis. Implement this filter and introduce a step change in the corresponding disturbance variable that was effectively removed from the process model. This will examine the effect of unmeasured disturbances on state estimation.

8.7 References

Hamilton, J. C., Seborg, D. E., and Fisher, D. G. (1973), "An experimental evaluation of Kalman filtering", *AIChEJ*, Vol. 19, No. 5, pp. 901–9.

9 Deadtime compensation

9.1 Introduction

It is well known that deadtime makes processes difficult to control. The large amount of phase lag destabilizes the control loop and well damped responses are difficult to obtain.

The idea of a deadtime compensator (DTC) was put forward by O. Smith (1957) and it is frequently described as a Smith predictor. The compensator is added to a standard control loop as shown in Figure 9.1. The form and positioning of the compensator effectively removes the deadtime from the dynamics of the loop resulting in a more stable system.

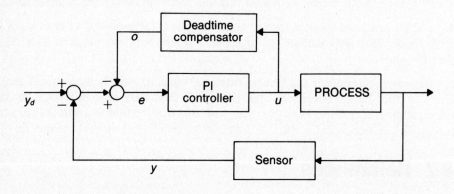

Figure 9.1 Deadtime compensator

9.2 Compensator design

The compensator takes the form of two models of the process, one including the deadtime and one without the deadtime. The compensator output is the difference between the two. For example, with a FOPDT model the delayed and nondelayed versions are:

$$y_1(kT_s)(1 + a_1q^{-1}) = b_0 u(kT_s - D)$$

$$y_2(kT_s)(1 + a_1q^{-1}) = b_0 u(kT_s)$$

The compensator output is:

$$o(kT_s) = y_2(kT_s) - y_1(kT_s)$$

and the modified error signal (see Figure 9.1) is:

$$e(kT_s) = y_d(kT_s) - y(kT_s) + o(kT_s)$$

where: $y_d(kT_s)$ is the setpoint.

The design process is therefore quite simple:

1. Obtain a process model including deadtime.
2. Design the compensator as shown above.
3. Implement and test the system.

One of the criticisms of the Smith predictor is that its performance is sensitive to the accuracy of the deadtime value within the compensator. Therefore some care should be taken in this regard, as is exemplified in the next section. If the deadtime varies with process operating conditions—not an uncommon problem—then the deadtime value should be made a function of these operating conditions.

9.3 Deadtime compensation on the evaporator

One of the difficulties in controlling the product composition $X2$ is an effective deadtime, in the response of $X2$, to changes in steam pressure $P100$. It is undoubtedly one of the factors that contribute to the destabilization of the product composition control loop $X2$–$P100$, the other factor being the interaction with the separator level control loop $L2$–$F2$. Control loop $X2$–$P100$ therefore appeared to be a good loop on which to test DTC.

The first step was to obtain a process model, by least-squares fitting of FOPDT and general second order models to a step response. The step was a 20 percent increase in

$P100$ with the separator level loop $L2$–$F2$ and the operating pressure loop $P2$–$F200$ in control. The two models obtained were:

$$y(k)(1 - 0.596q^{-1}) = 0.111u(k - 6)$$

and:

$$y(k)(1 - 1.60q^{-1} + 0.80q^{-2}) = 0.033(1 + 0.632q^{-1})\,u(k - 6)$$

Figure 9.2 shows the fit of the second order model to the step response of the nonlinear evaporator simulation.

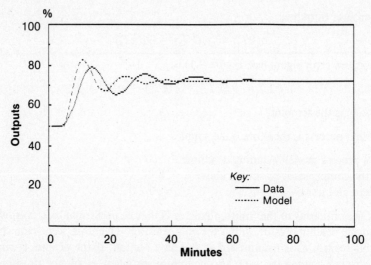

Figure 9.2 Fit of SOPDT model

The first tests of DTC used a deadtime of six minutes as selected by the least-squares fitting program. The first order DTC was more stable than feedback control alone, but the second order DTC proved to be unstable. The same feedback PI control constants were used throughout as determined in Chapter 4. If Figure 9.2 is examined, the actual process deadtime is probably about four minutes, so this was tried in place of the six minutes.

Figures 9.3 and 9.4 show the results of a test of the first order and second order DTCs compared to the uncompensated case shown in Figure 9.5. (A 10 percent decrease in feed flowrate $F1$ was used in each case.) In both cases the response was now more stable and, as might be expected, the second order compensator gave the better result. Settling times were approximately:

Feedback only ≈ 100 min
First Order DTC $\approx\ \ 60$ min
Second Order DTC $\approx\ \ 30$ min

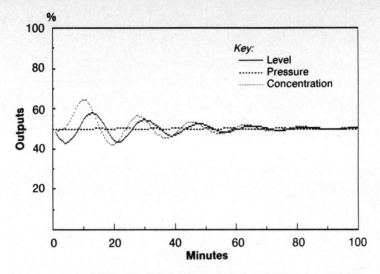

Figure 9.3 No deadtime compensation

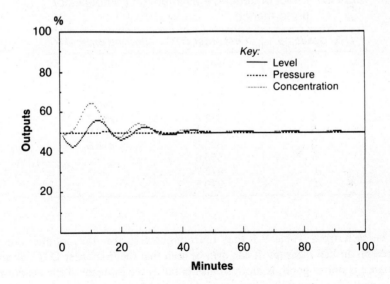

Figure 9.4 First-order deadtime compensated

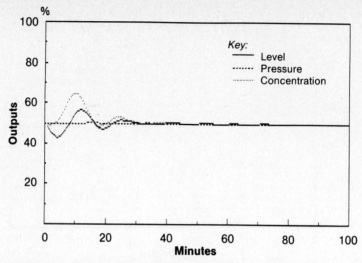

Figure 9.5 Second-order deadtime compensated

A study was then made of the sensitivity of the DTC to the estimate of the deadtime values, using the integral of the squared error of the product composition $X2$ as a measure. The results are shown in Table 9.1.

Table 9.1 Effect of deadtime estimate on compensator performance

DTC deadtime	First order DTC	Second order DTC
0	440.5	440.5
1	352.7	322.0
2	324.3	297.6
3	314.1	290.3
4	312.3	289.7
5	315.6	304.0
6	323.0	818.5
8	355.0	—
10	478.7	—
12	970.5	—

It can be seen from Table 9.1 that four minutes is also the optimal value when compared on an ISE measure. It can also be seen that the first order DTC, although its performance is not as good, is more robust as far as the estimate of the deadtime value is concerned. For example, Figures 9.6 and 9.7 show first and second order compensators with a six minute deadtime.

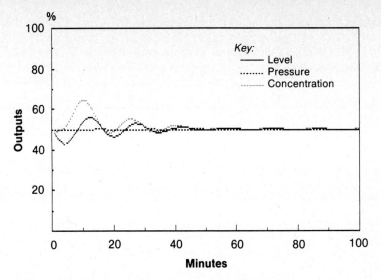

Figure 9.6 First-order 6-minute compensator

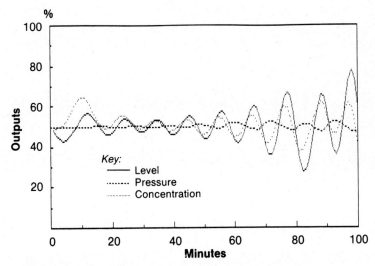

Figure 9.7 Second-order 6-minute compensator

9.4 Exercise

Suppose that the composition analyser used to measure $X2$ has a deadtime of three minutes in addition to the process effective deadtime. Design and implement a suitable DTC on the nonlinear model of the evaporator and compare it with feedback only control. You will also have to modify the nonlinear evaporator model to match this new time delay.

9.5 References

Smith, O. J. M. (1957), "Close control of loops with deadtime", *Chem. Eng. Prog.*, Vol. 53, No. 5, p. 217.

10 Adaptive control

10.1 Introduction

The problem of maintaining tight control over key variables, when process nonlinearities and changes in process characteristics occur, is well known. The practice of using fixed constants in any process controller in these circumstances is obviously not the best possible way of achieving good control.

In this chapter, we will examine two methods for improving the controller performance by "adapting" the controller constants to changing process characteristics.

10.2 Gain scheduling

In order to maintain constant control loop performance, the product:

$$K_c K_p = K_{ov}$$

where: K_c is the controller gain
K_p is the process gain
K_{ov} is the overall loop gain,

should remain constant. Obviously, if the process gain K_p is changing, then the controller gain should also change. This is the basis for "gain scheduling".

Usually, the process gain will change in a nonlinear manner. Hence the gain schedule for the controller gain should, in theory, be the inverse of this nonlinear function. This can usually be approximated by some simpler function, often constructed of linear segments, for example, the controller gain to be a simple function of the error signal to the controller.

An experimental procedure for determining an appropriate value of the controller gain schedule is:

1. Determine the open-loop gain at the desired operating point and at several points either side of this operating point.

73

2. Determine an appropriate value of the controller gain at the normal operating point to maintain good control in a small region about this operating point.
3. Construct an appropriate gain schedule for the controller by examining the change in the process gain determined in Step 1.

10.3 Application to the evaporator

The control of the exit concentration, $X2$, by adjusting the steam supply pressure, $P100$, exhibits nonlinear behavior. This was determined in Chapter 4 where for 20 percent step increases and decreases in $P100$, 40 percent variations in the process gain resulted.

A suitable gain schedule was constructed by evaluating the process gain at different values of the manipulated input, $P100$. These results are shown in Table 10.1 together with the controller gain used for the control loop obtained in Chapter 4.

Table 10.1 *Process gain schedule*

X2	Process gain	Controller gain	Overall gain
%			
35	0.421		
30	0.331		
25	0.234	1.64	0.384
20	0.257		
15	0.355		

The resulting controller gain is then given by:

$$K_c = 1.64 - (X2 - 25.0) * 0.065 \qquad X2 > 25 \qquad \textbf{(10.2)}$$

$$K_c = 1.64 - (25.0 - X2) * 0.065 \qquad X2 < 25 \qquad \textbf{(10.3)}$$

The response of the process using this gain-scheduled controller is shown in Figure 10.1. It can be seen that the controlled response has been considerably improved. This was confirmed by evaluating the integral of the absolute error multiplied by time (ITAE). The conventional controller shown in Figure 10.2 gave a value of approximately 16000, while the gain-scheduled controller gave a value of approximately 11000, a 30 percent improvement.

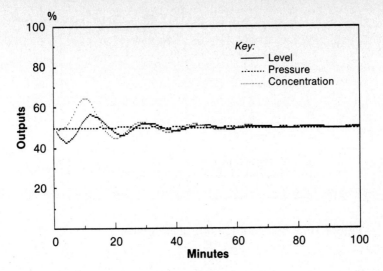

Figure 10.1 Gain scheduled controller

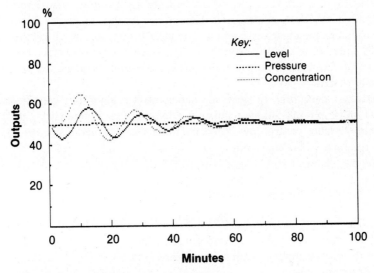

Figure 10.2 Standard PID control

10.4 Self-tuning controllers

A more rigorous approach to developing a controller that adapts to changing process characteristics is the self-tuning regulator. This more complex approach is necessary when process characteristics change with time in an indeterminate manner. The configuration of an adaptive controller is shown in Figure 10.3. The basic elements are:

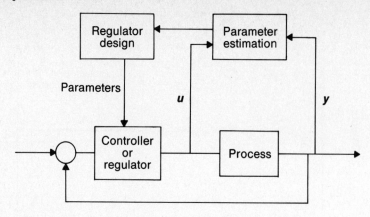

Figure 10.3 Self-tuning control structure

1. Identification of a simplified process model from input-output data. The model used is generally an ARMA model (refer Time Series Analysis, Chapter 3), with a form of least-squares parameter estimation. The identification of the model must proceed at a rate equal to, or slightly faster than, the change in process characteristics.
2. A means of calculating new controller parameters from the identified process model (regulator design).
3. A controller algorithm. In general, any controller algorithm can be used. The original work on self-tuning regulators (Astrom and Wittenmark 1973) used a minimum-variance control law. However more recent work (Cameron and Seborg 1983), has used a PID algorithm.

Given an ARMA model of the form:

$$A(z^{-1})y(t) = B(z^{-1})u(t - b - 1) + e(t) \qquad \textbf{(10.4)}$$

where: y is the process output deviation from setpoint
u is the process input deviation from steady-state
e is random noise
A and B are polynomials in the shift operator,

this model can be re-expressed as:

$$Y(t + b) = X^T(t)\hat{\Theta}(t) + e(t) \qquad \textbf{(10.5)}$$

where: $X^T(t) = [-y_{t-1}, -y_{t-2}, \ldots, -y_{t-n}; u_{t-1}, u_{t-2}, \ldots, u_{t-m}]$
$\hat{\Theta}(t) = [\hat{a}_1, \hat{a}_2, \ldots, \hat{a}_n; \hat{b}_0, \hat{b}_1, \ldots, \hat{b}_{m-1}]$

Least squares estimation of the model parameters can be obtained from the following recursive relations:

$$\hat{\underset{\sim}{\Theta}}(t) = \hat{\underset{\sim}{\Theta}}(t - 1) + \underset{\sim}{K}(t)[y(t) - \underset{\sim}{X}^T(t - b)\hat{\underset{\sim}{\Theta}}(t - 1)] \tag{10.6}$$

$$\underset{\sim}{K}(t) = \frac{\underset{\sim}{P}(t - 1)\,\underset{\sim}{X}(t - b)}{\lambda + \underset{\sim}{X}^T(t - b)\,\underset{\sim}{P}(t - 1)\,\underset{\sim}{X}(t - b)} \tag{10.7}$$

$$\underset{\sim}{P}(t) = \frac{1}{\lambda}\left[\underset{\sim}{P}(t - 1) - \frac{\underset{\sim}{P}(t - 1)\,\underset{\sim}{X}(t - b)\,\underset{\sim}{X}^T(t - b)\,\underset{\sim}{P}(t - 1)}{\lambda + \underset{\sim}{X}^T(t - b)\,\underset{\sim}{P}(t - 1)\,\underset{\sim}{X}(t - b)}\right] \tag{10.8}$$

The scalar factor, λ, $0 \leqslant \lambda \leqslant 1$, is the exponential discount factor. This factor weights past values of the process information vector $\underset{\sim}{X}$. A value of 1 implies all values are weighted equally, while a value near zero implies that only the more current values affect the parameter estimates. Thus, the exponential discount factor can be seen to influence the rate of adaption of the parameter estimates. In practice, $0.95 \leqslant \lambda \leqslant 0.99$ is usually used.

Although the recursive least-squares relations could be used as given, there are better numerical methods for performing these calculations. One such method is due to Bierman (1976) and is known as UD factorization. The subsequent application in this chapter will use this numerical method. The details of this method are contained in the original cited reference (Bierman 1976), including a FORTRAN computer program for implementation.

Another enhancement of the above algorithm is to allow the exponential discount factor λ to vary. This variation should allow the parameter estimates to adapt more rapidly when the process is disturbed and less rapidly when the process remains at setpoint under good control. A method for achieving this is outlined by Fortescue, Kershenbaum and Ydstie (1981) and has been used in this study. Details of this method are contained in the cited reference.

The remaining two parts of an adaptive controller, controller design and controller algorithm, are of course closely linked. The early work in this field mainly used a minimum variance control law. However, since in the process industries PID control is very popular, this case study will use a form of adaptive PID control. This has been outlined previously by Cameron and Seborg (1983).

In this approach the process is modeled as:

$$\hat{a}_0 y_f(t) + \hat{a}_1 y_f(t - 1) + \hat{a}_2 y_f(t - 2) = \frac{1}{\nu}\Delta u(t) \tag{10.9}$$

where: y_f is a "filtered" value of the process output deviation from setpoint
Δu is the change in the process input
ν is a design parameter that allows tuning of the controller.

A first-order filter is used to "filter" the process output signal:

$$y_f(t) = y(t) - p_d y_f(t - 1) \tag{10.10}$$

Given this model, the PID constants are given by:

$$K_c = -\nu(2\hat{a}_2 + \hat{a}_1)/\alpha \qquad (10.11)$$

$$T_I = T_s K_c/\{\nu\hat{a}_0/\alpha - K_c - K_c(T_D/T_s)\} \qquad (10.12)$$

$$T_D = T_s\nu\hat{a}_2/\alpha K_c \qquad (10.13)$$

$$\alpha = 1 + p_d \qquad (10.14)$$

$$-1 \leqslant p_d \leqslant 0$$

where: K_c = proportional gain
T_I = integral time
T_D = derivative time
T_s = sample interval.

A FORTRAN program to implement a self-tuning controller with PID structure is available (see Appendix A). This program includes a subroutine for least-squares parameter estimation using a variable forgetting factor and UD factorization.

10.5 Application to the evaporator

The result of applying the self-tuning controller to the $X2-P100$ control loop is shown in Figure 10.4. This result can be compared with the results obtained using conventional PID control shown in Figure 10.2. The controlled performance can be seen to be much improved. This is confirmed by comparing the ITAE values of 9700 for self-tuning control and 16000 for conventional PID control, an improvement of 40 percent.

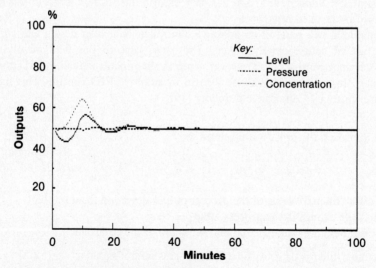

Figure 10.4 Self-tuning regulator

10.6 Exercises

1. The pressure control loop ($P2$—$F200$) also exhibits nonlinearity (refer Chapter 4). Design and implement a suitable gain scheduled controller for this loop and compare the results with those obtained in Chapter 4.

2. Design and implement a self-tuning controller for the $P2$—$F200$ loop and compare the results with a conventional PID controller.

10.7 References

Astrom, K. J. and Wittenmark, B. (1973), "On self-tuning regulators", *Automatica*, Vol. 9, pp. 185–99.

Bierman, G. J. (1976), "Measurement updating using the U-D factorization", *Automatica*, Vol. 12, pp. 375–82.

Cameron, F. and Seborg, D. E. (1983), "A self-tuning controller with a PID structure", *International Journal of Control*, Vol. 38, No. 2, pp. 401–17.

Fortescue, T. R., Kershenbaum, L. S. and Ydstie, B. E. (1981), "Implementation of self-tuning regulators with variable forgetting factors", *Automatica*, Vol. 17, No. 6, pp. 831–5.

11 Predictive control

11.1 Introduction

Since the early 1980s, predictive control has received much attention in the literature. This new type of multivariable controller has been successfuly applied to many industrial processes using two major approaches—Dynamic Matrix Control (DMC) and Model Algorithmic Control (MAC) (Cutler and Ramaker 1980; Richalet, Rault, Testud and Papon 1978). Both of these approaches are similar in concept and have many common features.

More recently, more efficient and robust design methods have been developed (Maurath, Mellichamp & Seborg 1985) and applied successfully to a number of pilot-scale processes (Callaghan 1986).

11.2 Convolution model

The application of most multivariable control methods requires the use of a process model. The model used in predictive control is an input-output model expressed as a convolution of impulse or step responses.

To obtain such a model, the usual practice would be to step test each input in turn and record the response of each process output. The step responses can then be used directly to obtain the convolution model. This is shown in Figure 11.1 for a single input–single output case.

At each sample time, the value of the step response of the output variable is known as the step response weight a_i. The difference between successive step response weights:

$$h_i = a_i - a_{i-1} \tag{11.1}$$

is known as the impulse response weight. Thus the value of the output variable y, at any sample time k, can be expressed as:

$$y_k = \sum_{i=1}^{N} h_i \, \Delta u_{k-i} \tag{11.2}$$

where N is the number of impulse response weights.

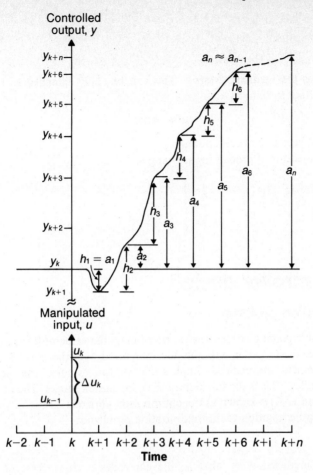

Figure 11.1 The response of a system at steady state to a step change in input yielding impulse and step response (convolution model) coefficients

Alternatively, this can be expressed in the form:

$$y_1 = a_1 \, \Delta u_1$$

$$y_2 = a_2 \, \Delta u_1 + a_1 \, \Delta u_2 \qquad\qquad (11.3)$$

$$y_3 = a_3 \, \Delta u_1 + a_2 \, \Delta u_2 + a_1 \, \Delta u_3$$

where the subscript refers to the sample time.

More generally:

$$\underset{\sim}{y} = \underset{\approx}{A}\,\underset{\sim}{\Delta u} \qquad\qquad (11.4)$$

$$\text{where: } \underset{\sim}{A} = \begin{bmatrix} a_1 & 0 & 0 \\ a_2 & a_1 & 0 \\ a_3 & a_2 & a_1 \end{bmatrix}$$

and is known as the Dynamic Matrix. This can be easily extended to multiple-input and multiple-output systems as:

$$\underset{\sim}{y} = \underset{\sim}{A}\Delta\underset{\sim}{u} \tag{11.5}$$

where: $\underset{\sim}{y}$ is the vector of process outputs.

$\Delta\underset{\sim}{u}$ is the vector of process input changes.

$$\underset{\sim}{A} = \begin{bmatrix} \underset{\sim}{A}_{11} & \underset{\sim}{A}_{12} & \cdots & \underset{\sim}{A}_{1n} \\ \underset{\sim}{A}_{21} & \underset{\sim}{A}_{22} & \cdots & \underset{\sim}{A}_{2n} \\ \underset{\sim}{A}_{m1} & \underset{\sim}{A}_{m2} & \cdots & \underset{\sim}{A}_{mn} \end{bmatrix}$$

11.4 Controller design

The optimization problem

The control problem can be expressed as determining the value of $\underset{\sim}{u}$ such that the error between the outputs and their setpoints are minimized over the next R future sample times. This statement automatically implies that we can "predict" the future values of the output variables. This is the function of the convolution model. The number of time steps into the future, R, is known as the optimization horizon.

The best possible solution to this optimization problem is:

$$\Delta\underset{\sim}{u} = \underset{\sim}{A}^{-1}\underset{\sim}{e} \tag{11.6}$$

where $\underset{\sim}{e}$ is the predicted error, that is, the controller is the inverse of the process. However, in practise this will lead to very severe control action, often leading to instability.

Consequently, the optimization problem is altered such that the problem is to determine L control moves that minimize the predicted error over R future values, where L is less than R. This implies that the matrix $\underset{\sim}{A}$ is now no longer square and we find the solution as:

$$\Delta\underset{\sim}{u} = (\underset{\sim}{A}^T\underset{\sim}{A})^{-1}\underset{\sim}{A}^T\underset{\sim}{e} \tag{11.7}$$

where: $(\underset{\sim}{A}^T\underset{\sim}{A})^{-1}\underset{\sim}{A}^T$ is known as the "pseudo-inverse" or least-squares solution (Penrose 1956).

In practice this is usually further modified by considering:

1. different weightings on different output variables. This allows for scaling problems with different outputs and for the importance of one output over another;
2. input move weighting. This allows the control input moves to be weighted or penalized, thus introducing some reduction in control action.

With these two modifications, the solution becomes:

$$\Delta \underset{\sim}{u} = (\underset{\sim}{A}^T \underset{\sim}{Q} \underset{\sim}{A} + \underset{\sim}{R})^{-1} \underset{\sim}{A}^T \underset{\sim}{Q} \underset{\sim}{e} \tag{11.8}$$

where: $\underset{\sim}{Q}$ is the process output weighting matrix and $\underset{\sim}{R}$ is the input weighting matrix.

Singular value decomposition

Singular value decomposition (SVD) is a powerful numerical technique which can be applied to the problem of calculating the pseudo-inverses of matrices. The method has very good numerical properties and can provide further insight into the design procedure, as shown in the following section on principal component analysis.

The SVD of a matrix $\underset{\sim}{Q}\underset{\sim}{A}$ can be expressed as:

$$\underset{\sim}{Q}\underset{\sim}{A} = \underset{\sim}{U}\underset{\sim}{\Sigma}\underset{\sim}{V}^T \tag{11.9}$$

where: $\underset{\sim}{U}$ and $\underset{\sim}{V}$ are orthogonal, normalized vectors

$$\underset{\sim}{\Sigma} = \begin{bmatrix} \underset{\sim}{S} \\ \hline \underset{\sim}{0} \end{bmatrix}$$

where: $\underset{\sim}{S}$ is a matrix of the positive square roots of the eigenvalues of the matrix $\underset{\sim}{Q}\underset{\sim}{A}$ known as the "singular values" (σ_i).

Given the SVD of the matrix $\underset{\sim}{Q}\underset{\sim}{A}$, then the solution to the optimization problem becomes:

$$\Delta \underset{\sim}{u} = (\underset{\sim}{V}\underset{\sim}{\Sigma}^{+}\underset{\sim}{U}^T)\underset{\sim}{Q}\underset{\sim}{e} \tag{11.10}$$

where: $\underset{\sim}{\Sigma}^{+} = [\underset{\sim}{S}^{-1} \mid \underset{\sim}{0}]$ providing $\underset{\sim}{Q}\underset{\sim}{A}$ is of full rank.

There are many good numerical computer codes available to calculate the SVD of a matrix.

Principal component analysis

The design of a predictive controller using Principal Component Analysis (PCA) has recently been outlined (Maurath et al. 1985). The original optimization problem can be expressed as:

$$\text{minimize } J(\underset{\sim}{w}) = \| \underset{\sim}{\Sigma}\underset{\sim}{w} - \underset{\sim}{g} \|^2 \text{ with respect to } \underset{\sim}{w} \tag{11.11}$$

and expanded as:

$$J(\underset{\sim}{w}) = \sum_{i=1}^{n_2} (\sigma_i w_i - g_i)^2 + \sum_{i=1}^{n_1} g_i^2 \tag{(11.12}$$

where: $\underset{\sim}{w} = \underset{\sim}{V}^T \Delta \underset{\sim}{u}$
$\underset{\sim}{g} = \underset{\sim}{U}^T \underset{\sim}{Q} \underset{\sim}{e}$

The elements of the $\underset{\sim}{w}$ vector are the principal components of the solution to the least-squares problem. Each element contributes to improving the solution by reducing the residual. If the ith component is excluded from the solution ($\underset{\sim}{w}_i = 0$), the residual increases by g_i^2. Each component used in the solution also increases the norm (size) of the $\underset{\sim}{w}$ vector by w_i^2. In a poorly conditioned problem the components which correspond to small singular values contribute very little to reducing the residual (g_i^2 is small) but they greatly increase the norm of the $\underset{\sim}{w}$ vector. By eliminating these components a less severe and less sensitive solution is obtained.

Design procedure for principal component analysis

This section is drawn mainly from Maurath et al. (1985). The first step is to perform an SVD on the $Q\underset{\sim}{A}$ matrix. From the previous section on principal component analysis, we see that to evaluate the residual vector g it is necessary to know $\underset{\sim}{e}$, the error vector. For a thorough design, $\underset{\sim}{e}$ is generated for a unit setpoint change in every output, that is, for a 2 output system two tests are performed with:

$$\underset{\sim}{e}_1 = (1, 1, \ldots 1, 0, 0, \ldots 0)^T$$
$$e_2 = (0, 0, \ldots 0, 1, 1, \ldots 1)^T$$
(11.13)

For each setpoint change the g and $\underset{\sim}{u}$ vectors are formed. A table is then constructed to aid the designer. For each setpoint change this can consist of:

1. the associated singular value, σ_i;
2. the contribution that individual component make toward reducing the residual, $(G_F)_i$;
3. the remaining residual, $(G_S)_i$, assuming this and all previous values are retained, and the rest are discarded;
4. the first control move in each variable, u_1 assuming this and all previous values are retained, and the rest are discarded.

The normalised residual columns can be calculated by:

$$(G_F)_i = g_i^2 / \underset{\sim}{g}^T \underset{\sim}{g}$$
(11.14)

$$(G_S)_i = 1 - \sum_{j=1}^{i} g_j^2 / \underset{\sim}{g}^T \underset{\sim}{g}$$
(11.15)

For a 2 input system the first control move in the first manipulated variable can be calculated by:

$$\Delta u_1 = \sum_{j=1}^{i} V_{1,i}\, g_i / \sigma_i$$
(11.16)

and the first move in the second manipulated variable:

$$\Delta u_{L+1} = \sum_{j=1}^{i} V_{L+1,i}\, g_i / \sigma_i$$
(11.17)

The first input changes are used rather than the norm of the solution vector, as they can be compared to the final steady state inputs for the step change being considered. A general rule of thumb is that the initial change should not exceed two or three times the steady-state change in each input. The system designer can make a trade-off between control system performance, quantified by G_s, and control input energy, quantified by Δu_1. Lower values of Δu_1 contribute to increased robustness. The final value of G_s also indicates the limit of control using the specified R and L values selected. If the final G_s value is low there is little incentive to expand either of the horizons. If the final G_s value is high then obviously one or both of the horizons should be extended until the value reaches an acceptable lower limit.

Design guidelines for predictive controllers designed by principal component analysis

Design of any predictive controller using the component selection method is strongly dependent on the individual process. Some guidelines given by Maurath et al. (1985) were:

1. The only requirements on L and R are that they should not be too small. L should extend over the significant adjustments in the manipulated variable required to implement a setpoint change. R should include 80 to 90 percent of the rise to a new steady state in an open-loop step response.
2. The first control move in the design table should not be more than two or three times the steady state input changes for each input.
3. Components which do not contribute to control improvement, or which produce larger than acceptable control inputs, should not be included in the controller. A suggested guideline to determine whether a component significantly improves control is whether the normalised residual reduction, G_F, exceeds $1/(4R)$. For MIMO applications this criterion must be examined for all outputs.

Cutler (1983) recommends setting L to cover a time equal to the deadtime plus the time for the output response from a step change in the manipulated input to reach 60 percent of its steady state value, that is, deadtime plus the major (pseudo-1st-order) time constant. The above time is divided into 5 to 15 moves in the manipulated input. Note that typically N is in the region of 20 to 50.

For MIMO systems with time constants orders of magnitude different, it has been recommended (Callaghan and Lee, 1986) that R, L and T_s should be set for the faster dynamics, as the smaller time constants appear to be more important. The prediction length N, however, should be set to accommodate the slowest dynamics.

Robustness

A major concern of any controller designed on the basis of a process model is how susceptible they are to modeling errors. Since the convolution model is a linear approximation to the general nonlinear process, model inaccuracies arise naturally for most processes. For example, the response of the output variables may alter for a step increase as opposed to step decrease in an input variable. The ability of a controller to cope with such problems is called the "robustness" of the controller.

Consider an average response model:

$$\tilde{a}_i = \frac{a_i(\max) + a_i(\min)}{2} \tag{11.18}$$

where the a_i represent step response weights.

Then the normal procedure would be to design a predictive controller based on this average response model $\tilde{a}_i$. The modeling error may be expressed as:

$$\Delta a_i = \tilde{a}_i - a_i(\max) \tag{11.19}$$

Given this information, and the singular value decomposition vector $\underset{\sim}{V}$, a criterion for robustness (Grimm, Lee and Callaghan 1988) is:

$$S_j = \sum_{i=1}^{R} \sum_{m=1}^{NP} \Delta a_i^2(m, j) \tag{11.20}$$

where: NP is the number of outputs.

Then for robustness:

$$\left(\sum_{i=1}^{M} \frac{1}{\sigma_i^2(\tilde{A})} \right) \sum_{j=1}^{NM} V^2_{[(j-1)L+1,i]} S_j < 1 \tag{11.21}$$

where: NM is the number of inputs

M is the number of retained singular values in the principal component analysis.

This condition must be evaluated to determine the maximum number of singular values to be retained in the controller design, while still retaining robust characteristics.

For a two input–two output system the criterion can be expressed as:

$$S_1 = \sum_{i=1}^{R} \Delta a_i(1, 1)^2 + \sum_{i=1}^{R} \Delta a_i(2, 1)^2 \tag{11.22}$$

$$S_2 = \sum_{i=1}^{R} \Delta a_i(1, 2)^2 + \sum_{i=1}^{R} \Delta a_i(2, 2)^2 \tag{11.23}$$

Then:

$$\sum_{i=1}^{M} \frac{1}{\sigma_i^2(\tilde{A})} \{ V_{1,i}^2 S_1 + V_{L+1,i}^2 S_2 \} < 1 \tag{11.24}$$

11.4 Implementation of predictive control

The robustness of the predictive controller, allowing for modeling inaccuracies, is due to the feedback compensation applied at each time step. This adjusts for discrepancies between the predicted process output and the real plant measurements. Other important features are the initialization and the adjustment of the end of the prediction. The outline below is basically the same as that of DMC (Cutler and Ramaker 1980, Cutler 1983). The predictive controller is implemented in the following manner:

1. A prediction vector, p, of length $N + 1$ is set to the current measurement for all outputs. The prediction vector consists of estimates of the future output at future sample times calculated from the present. Thus, $p(i)_k$ is the prediction i sampling times in the future, from the current time k.

2. Time is progressed by one sampling time. The difference between the predicted value for the current time and the actual output of the current time, y_k is added to all elements of the prediction vector. The prediction vector is then moved forward one time interval, that is:

$$p(i)_k = p(i + 1)_{k-1} + y_k - p(1)_k \qquad (11.25)$$

This calculation acts as the feedback correction in predictive control.

3. The current error vector, e, between the setpoint and the prediction over the next R sampling periods is calculated.

4. The control move is calculated for each input, using its particular row or subset vector K^T of the $V\Sigma^+ U^T Q$ matrix, by:

$$\Delta u = K^T e \qquad (11.26)$$

and is implemented.

5. The first N values of the prediction vector are then updated to compensate for the control move just implemented. This can be done using any model, but since the step responses have been obtained and the on-line computation is quick, the step response coefficients are most used, that is:

$$p(i) = p(i) + a_i \Delta u \qquad (11.27)$$

6. If the system has a finite step response function, then the last value of the prediction is set equal to the second last, that is:

$$p(N + 1) = p(N) \qquad (11.28)$$

If this is not the case some function is used to calculate the last value in the prediction, that is, for a system whose steady state is a constant rate of change:

$$p(N + 1) = p(N) + (p(N) - p(N - 1)) \qquad (11.29)$$

7. The algorithm returns to Step 2.

11.5 Application to the evaporator

The application of predictive control, as described above, to the evaporator described in Chapter 2 was carried out using available design and simulation programs (refer Appendix A). The application used the following design values:

Prediction horizon – N	150
Optimization horizon – R	50
Control horizon – L	25
Sample time	1 minute

Using these values a series of step tests were conducted on the evaporator. In these step tests the level control loop *L2–F2* was operated under closed-loop control while the concentration and pressure control loops (*X2* and *P2*) were not implemented.

The responses of the exit concentration *X2* and the pressure *P2* were recorded for 10 percent increases and decreases in the steam supply pressure *P100* and the cooling water flowrate *F200*. The results of these step-up and step-down responses were arithmetically averaged to produce the required step coefficients for the dynamic matrix model. This model, together with the design values given above, were then used to perform a principal component analysis using an available computer program (refer Appendix A). The results of this analysis are shown in Table 11.1. This table indicates that the value of G_f falls to zero somewhere between ten and fifteen singular values, indicating that this many values should be retained in the final controller design to obtain reasonable performance.

Performance of the designed controller is not the only consideration. The robust properties of the proposed controller should also be investigated. Using the methods outlined in this chapter in the section on robustness, the robustness of the proposed controller was examined. The results of this examination are shown in Table 11.2. It can be seen from this table that the criterion for robustness exceeds the critical value of one after 13 singular values. Thus, 12 singular values are recommended to maintain good control, despite the differences in the behavior of the system for step increases and decreases.

Table 11.1 Principal component analysis

Analysis for X2

I	σ_i	G_F	G_S	P100	F200
1	99.017	0.695	0.305	0.013	0.001
2	31.231	0.016	0.289	0.020	-0.001
3	19.601	0.017	0.272	0.029	-0.000
4	17.910	0.136	0.136	0.021	0.035
5	16.064	0.036	0.100	0.041	0.042
6	11.372	0.011	0.090	0.064	0.041
7	5.902	0.018	0.071	0.126	0.042
8	3.070	0.000	0.071	0.120	0.049
9	2.732	0.024	0.047	0.230	0.126
10	1.459	0.009	0.038	0.374	0.113
11	0.813	0.008	0.030	0.491	0.323
12	0.792	0.002	0.028	0.581	0.246
13	0.482	0.006	0.022	0.819	0.264
14	0.345	0.000	0.022	0.810	0.346
15	0.318	0.004	0.018	1.069	0.444
16	0.224	0.003	0.015	1.329	0.416
17	0.185	0.000	0.014	1.340	0.657
18	0.164	0.002	0.012	1.602	0.634
19	0.125	0.002	0.010	1.860	0.703
20	0.114	0.000	0.010	1.855	0.827

Analysis for P2

I	σ_i	G_F	G_S	P100	F200
1	99.017	0.125	0.875	0.006	0.000
2	31.231	0.075	0.799	0.021	-0.003
3	19.601	0.000	0.799	0.022	-0.003
4	17.910	0.438	0.361	0.036	-0.067
5	16.064	0.036	0.325	0.016	-0.074
6	11.372	0.006	0.319	0.033	-0.075
7	5.902	0.000	0.319	0.035	-0.075
8	3.070	0.122	0.197	0.218	-0.268
9	2.732	0.058	0.139	0.042	-0.391
10	1.459	0.002	0.137	0.108	-0.397
11	0.813	0.038	0.099	-0.154	-0.868
12	0.792	0.021	0.077	0.129	-1.109
13	0.482	0.000	0.077	0.135	-1.109
14	0.345	0.027	0.050	0.254	-2.175
15	0.318	0.001	0.050	0.159	-2.211
16	0.224	0.000	0.049	0.239	-2.220
17	0.185	0.015	0.034	0.176	-3.651
18	0.164	0.000	0.034	0.248	-3.658
19	0.125	0.000	0.034	0.230	-3.663
20	0.114	0.009	0.025	0.295	-5.380

Table 11.2 Robustness analysis

I	σ_1	V_1	V_2	Criterion of equation (11.24)
1	0.9902×10^{-1}	-0.2230×10^{-1}	-0.1300×10^{-1}	0.1677×10^{-4}
2	0.3123×10^{-1}	0.2540×10^{-1}	-0.5200×10^{-1}	0.2396×10^{-3}
3	0.1960×10^{-1}	-0.2030×10^{-1}	-0.1100×10^{-1}	0.5941×10^{-3}
4	0.1791×10^{-1}	0.5300×10^{-1}	-0.2520×10^{-1}	0.9476×10^{-3}
5	0.1606×10^{-1}	-0.2440×10^{-1}	-0.8400×10^{-1}	0.1754×10^{-2}
6	0.1137×10^{-1}	0.3720×10^{-1}	-0.1600×10^{-1}	0.5288×10^{-2}
7	0.5902×10^{-1}	-0.4040×10^{-1}	-0.1100×10^{-1}	0.2076×10^{-1}
8	0.3070×10^{-1}	0.2330×10^{-1}	-0.2450×10^{-1}	0.5021×10^{-1}
9	0.2732×10^{-1}	-0.2880×10^{-1}	-0.2010×10^{-1}	0.9576×10^{-1}
10	0.1459×10^{-1}	0.3200×10^{-1}	-0.2900×10^{-1}	0.2552
11	0.8130×10^{-1}	-0.1570×10^{-1}	-0.2830×10^{-1}	0.5769
12	0.7920×10^{-1}	0.2210×10^{-1}	-0.1890×10^{-1}	0.9273
13	0.4820×10^{-1}	-0.2230×10^{-1}	-0.1800×10^{-1}	$0.1636 \times 10^{+1}$

Choose $M = 12$

The control horizon, $L = 25$
The sum of squares #1 of the deviation matrix = 3.3
The sum of squares #2 of the deviation matrix = 1.64

The results of applying the predictive controller are shown in Figure 11.2, while the results of using the PI control strategy developed in Chapter 4 are shown for comparison in Figure 11.3. The predictive controller retained 13 singular values in the design procedure. These figures show the response of the evaporator to a step change in

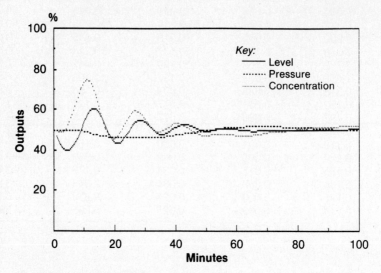

Figure 11.2 Predictive control

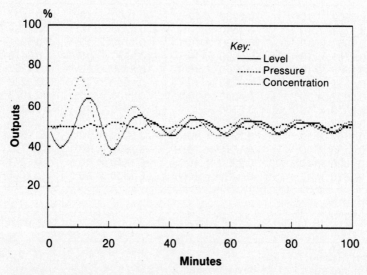

Figure 11.3 Standard PI control

the inlet feed flowrate from 10 kg/min to 8.5 kg/min. It can be seen from these figures that the predictive controller performs considerably better than the PI control strategy. This was quantified by evaluating the integral of the absolute error multiplied by the time (ITAE) for the exit concentration $X2$. The PI controller returned a value of 7700 while the predictive controller had a value of 5300, a 30 percent improvement.

11.6 Exercises

1. The evaporator described in Chapter 2 of this book has strong interactions between single loop controllers (see Chapter 4). A multivariable controller is one means of obtaining better control of such processes. For this evaporator, obtain a convolution model in dynamic matrix form using the steam supply pressure $P100$ and the cooling water flowrate $F200$ as process inputs, and the evaporator pressure $P2$ and product concentration $X2$ as process outputs. You will need to consider:

1. the sampling time, T_s;
2. how many samples to retain in your model, N.

It has been found that NT_s should be chosen to cover the full response of the system.

2. The design of the above predictive controller assumed a number of defined design parameters—the prediction horizon, the optimization horizon, the control horizon, the sample time and the number of retained singular values. Choose a number of these parameters and investigate their effect on the controller performance.

11.7 References

Callaghan, P. J. (196), "An experimental investigation of predictive controller design by principal component analysis", M.Eng.Sci. thesis, Univ. of Queensland.

Callaghan, P. J. and Lee, P. L. (1986), "Multivariable predictive control of a grinding circuit", *Proc. 3rd Australian Control Conf.*, Sydney, pp. 99–104.

Cutler, C. R. (1983), "Dynamic matrix control: An optimal multivariable algorithm with constraints", Ph.D. thesis, Univ. of Houston.

Cutler, C. R. and Ramaker, B. L. (1980), "Dynamic matrix control—a computer control algorithm", *Proc. Automatic Control Conf.*, USA Paper WP5-B.

Grimm, W. M., Lee, P. L. and Callaghan, P. J. (1988), "Practical robust predictive control of a heat exchange network", *Chem. Eng. Commun.*, (in press).

Maurath, P. R., Mellichamp, D. A. and Seborg, D. E. (1985), "Predictive controller design by principal components analysis", *Proc. Automatic Control Conf.*, USA, pp. 1059–65.

Penrose, R. (1956), "On the best approximate solutions of linear matrix equations", *Proc. Cambridge Philos. Soc.*, Vol. 52, No. 1, pp. 17–19.

Richalet, J., Rault, A., Testud, J. L. and Papon, J. (1978), "Model predictive heuristic control: applications to industrial processes", *Automatica*, Vol. 14, pp. 413–28.

12 Constraint control

12.1 Introduction

Constraint control (Maarleveld and Rijnsdorp 1970) is possibly the most common "advanced" computer control technique used in the chemical processing industry. References describing its applications are plentiful; one such reference is Kane (1987).

Early studies of the optimization of processing units invariably found that there is a restricted feasible operating space bounded by various process constraints. Further, the optimal operating point is generally in one corner, up against the constraints defining that corner.

Unfortunately it is not simply a case of setting process set-points at those conditions and having an optimal operating process. There are two problems which make the situation more complex. Firstly, the process is subject to disturbances which, if th operating point is chosen too close to the constraint values, may result in the constraint values being exceeded. Secondly, it is unusual for the constraints to remain stationary with the usual changes in operating and environmental conditions. The solution of the plant operators is to keep away from the constraints. But that also keeps operation away from the optimal operating point and hence costs money.

With the advent of the process computer, which can observe the process more frequently, more consistently and without getting tired, the concept of constraint control could be applied. The concept is simply to measure the position of the constraints and manipulate process setpoints to keep close to, but at a safe distance from them.

12.2 The design of constraint control systems

There are five well defined steps to the design of a constraint control system. These will be discussed briefly below and the next section will present an example. The steps are:

1. Determine the degrees of freedom which define the dimension of the operating space. These include manipulated variables not used by the normal control system and the setpoints of control loops which maintain important operating conditions.

2. Determine the constraints which define the boundaries of the feasible operating space. These constraints may be equipment constraints, such as maximum and minimum pumping rates and safe operating temperatures and pressures. They may also be processing constraints to avoid damage to the material being processed, such as coking of heavy petroleum oils or denaturing of the protein in foodstuffs.

3. Determine the optimal operating point. This is a classical optimization problem. Firstly define an objective function, in this case a process operating cost, and then search the feasible operating space for the point which minimizes this cost. The search may be heuristic in nature or, for bigger problems, may require a constrained optimization technique applied to the process itself or a model of the process.

4. Design a constraint control system, usually one loop for every dimension of the operating space. This involves determining a simple or inferred measurement which indicates how close the process is to each constraint and then pairing these with the degrees of freedom. The type of controller used depends upon the importance of the constraint and how close to and how rapidly the process can move. Generally, quite slow adjustments by integral only controllers will suffice. An exception to this is on the surge control of compressors, where the process can quickly move into a potentially very damaging constraint so that quite sophisticated gain-scheduled, fast-acting algorithms are generally used.

5. Finally it simply remains to implement and test the measurements and lastly the controllers.

12.3 Constraint control on the evaporator

This example will be presented following the five design steps outlined above.

Consider the evaporator with complete mass and energy balance controls ($L2$ by $F2$, $P2$ by $F200$) and quality control ($X2$ by $P100$ with feedforward from $F1$). Also consider that feed conditions ($F1$, $X1$ and $T1$) are determined by upstream processing and the environment ($T200$) is constant.

1. The one manipulated variable not used by the standard control system is the circulating flowrate $F3$. Of the controller setpoints, $L2$ has no effect on the process operation, $P2$ can be adjusted and $X2$ is determined by product quality requirements. Hence the operating space is two dimensional being defined by $F3$ and $P2$.

2. The obvious constraints on the circulating flowrate $F3$ are the minimum (0 kg/min) and maximum (100 kg/min) pumping rates. However if $F3$ is reduced, then the heat transfer coefficient in the steam heater also falls, requiring a larger temperature driving force to maintain the duty, which in turn implies that the eventual limit is a wide open steam control valve (maximum steam pressure of 400 kPa). If $F3$ is increased so too is the process gain in the $X2$–$P100$ control loop, causing increasing oscillation and eventually instability. Retuning could be used to overcome this constraint. The equipment limit on operating pressure $P2$ would be the vessel vacuum design limit. However, we will assume that processing constraints are tighter. Pressure $P2$ determines operating temperatures $T2$ and $T3$. If the pressure drops too low there is insufficient driving force in the condenser and the cooling water flow $F200$ reaches its maximum of 400 kg/min. Conversely, if the pressure rises too high there is insufficient driving force in the steam heater, hence the steam pressure reaches its maximum of 400 kPa. Figure 12.1 shows these three constraints.

3. If steam and electricity consumption are assumed to be the predominant operating costs, then the optimal operating point will be minimum recirculation (electricity) and minimum pressure (less preheating of feed to its boiling point). This would put the process against the steam heater and condenser constraints.

4. Being a two dimensional operating space, the optimum is against two constraints and hence needs two control loops to hold it there. It follows from the discussion in 2. above that the position of the heater constraint is determined by the average steam pressure and the position of the condenser constraint by the average cooling water flowrate. The instantaneous values will vary due to disturbances in the $X2$–$P100$ and $P2$–$F200$ control loops. In order to allow for control action for these loops, the constraint set-points were taken as 350, in place of the maximum 400 (a 12.5 percent control margin). The selection of manipulated setpoints is fairly obvious, giving constraint controllers $P100$–$F3$ and $F200$–$P2$.

5. The constraint controllers were implemented as integral only controllers with integral times of 500 minutes because these loops should operate an order of magnitude slower than the regulatory loops.

Figures 12.2 and 12.3 show the constraint control system in action. In Figure 12.2 the process started operation at time zero, at the standard operating conditions listed in Chapter 2 ($P2 = 50.5$ kPa, $F3 = 50$ kg/min and shown as Point 0 in Figure 12.1). The constraint control system brought the process up against the selected constraints with only a minor disturbance to product quality $X2$ ($P2 = 42$ kPa, $F3 = 22.8$ kg/min shown as Point 1 in Figure 12.1).

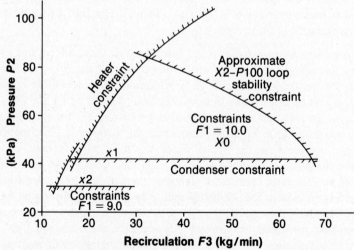

Figure 12.1 Feasible operating space

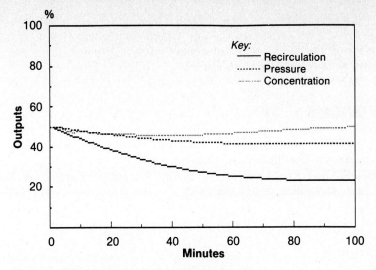

Figure 12.2 Moving against the constraints

In Figure 12.3 a step change in the feed flowrate $F1$ from 10 to 9 kg/min occurred at the start. The change in feed flowrate moved the process constraints so that the constraint controllers gradually brought the process up against the new constraints ($P2 = 32.1$ kPa, $F3 = 17.9$ kg/min shown as Point 2 in Figure 12.1). In Figure 12.3, the response of the regulatory controllers to the change in $F1$ can be seen imposed on the slower acting constraint control response.

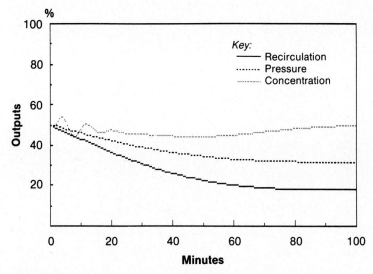

Figure 12.3 New constraints after feed change

12.4 Exercise

Design, implement and test a constraint control system assuming that the operating cost is dominated by the cost of cooling water.

References

Kane, L. (1987), *Handbook of Advanced Process Control Systems and Instrumentation*, Gulf Publishers, Houston, Tex.

Maarleveld, A. and Rijnsdorp, J. E. (1970), "Constraint Control on Distillation Columns", *Automatica*, Vol. 6, pp. 51–5.

13 Fuzzy heuristic control

13.1 Introduction

Much of the decision-making that we carry out from day to day is based upon qualitative, rather than quantitative, information. Decisions are arrived at using rough "rules-of-thumb", rather than precise mathematical equations. For example, many of the strategies employed in control and scheduling in an industrial plant cannot be described by standard mathematical equations. However, they can at least be written down in linguistic form, usually as a set of, *If... Then... Else...* rules. For instance, a human process operator controls the process using a strategy that consists of a set of linguistic rules, such as:

> If the temperature is high and rising,
> then increase the cooling a lot.

Fuzzy set theory is a mathematical tool for representing such rules in a manner suitable for implementation on a digital computer. It is an extension of classical set theory that provides a more realistic representation of imprecise linguistic values, such as "high", than does classical set theory.

In the last ten years, work has begun on the use of fuzzy set theory in process control applications. Most of this work has been concerned with representing the heuristic algorithms used by human process operators as a set of *If... Then... Else...* rules. The set of rules is then programmed into a digital computer, using fuzzy set theory as the mathematical representation, to form an automatic "fuzzy" control algorithm. This initial work has shown much promise.

The ability to use heuristic algorithms in automatic control allows computer control to be applied to processes that have so far defeated the use of standard automatic control algorithms. It also enables control systems to use fuzzy information from the operator where traditional measurements are not possible.

13.2 Fuzzy set theory

The concept of a fuzzy set (Zadeh 1965) is a simple extension of the notion of a classical set. With a classical set of objects an object either does, or does not, belong to the set. For a fuzzy set of objects, on the other hand, every object has a grade of membership in the set (Figure 13.1). The grade of membership arbitrarily runs from zero to one and is represented by a membership function $M(x)$ where x is the domain, or "universe of the discourse", of the set of all objects. Every object x has its own membership function value $m(x)$.

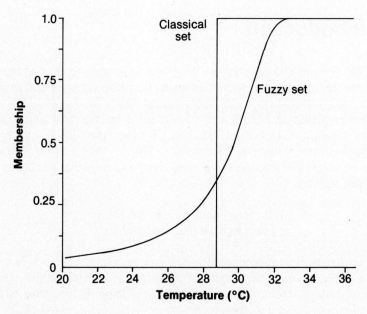

Figure 13.1 Classical set versus fuzzy set

Fuzzy set theory allows not only the representation of linguistic values, but also allows such values to be manipulated in a logical way. New fuzzy sets in the same domain can be formed using logical connectives such as "*and*" and "*or*" (Figure 13.2).

1. *Fuzzy sets A and B*

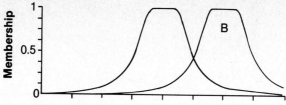

2. *Intersection of A and B*

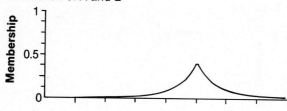

3. *Union of A and B*

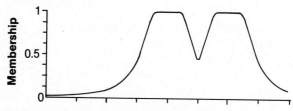

Figure 13.2 *"and"* and *"or"*

The mathematical relations for forming set C from sets A and B are:

$$C = A \text{ AND } B: \quad M_c(x) = \min (M_A(x), M_B(x))$$

$$C = A \text{ OR } B: \quad M_c(x) = \max (M_A(x), M_B(x))$$

Further, *If... Then...* rules can be evaluated to give an output fuzzy set in one domain from an input fuzzy set in another domain. The rules are also known as fuzzy relations. Mathematically the process for the rule *If A then B* is:

$$B = A \circ R: \quad M_B(y) = \overset{\max}{\underset{u}{}} (\min (M_A(u), M_R(u, y))$$

where: B is the fuzzy output set in y
   A is the fuzzy input set in u
   R is the fuzzy relation in the u, y domain.

Mathematically the relation membership matrix is defined as:

$$R = A' \times B': M_R(u, y) = \min (M_{A^1}(u), M_{B^1}(y))$$

where A' and B' are the defining fuzzy sets (Figure 13.3).

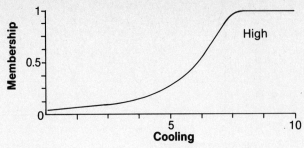

1. *Input fuzzy set* A′

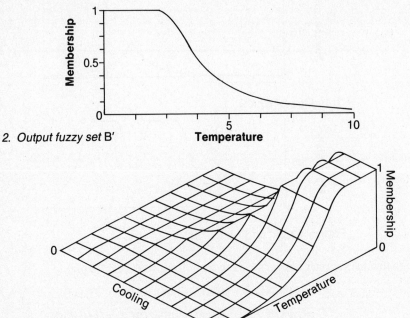

2. *Output fuzzy set* B′

3. *Fuzzy relation between input and output* R′ = A′ × B′)

Figure 13.3 A fuzzy relation

For compound conditional inputs, such as: *if A and B then C*, the relation is:

$$C = A \circ (B \circ R) \text{ where } R = A' \times B' \times C'$$

When the output of a set of rules is required, the output fuzzy sets of the individual rules must be combined. When considering *If... then... else...* rules the *else* can be treated as a logical *or* connective. The combining of fuzzy sets is shown in Figure 13.2. The fuzzy set that results is the output fuzzy set for the entire rule set. This technique of evaluating a set of rules is logically similar to the way in which a human would evaluate the rules.

13.3 Fuzzy heuristic control

Most of the work on fuzzy control has involved implementing a control strategy that consists of a set of *If... then... else* heuristic control rules. Fuzzy set theory allows these rules to be programmed directly into a digital computer to form a fuzzy heuristic control algorithm. Reviews of this work have been published by Maiers and Sherif (1985), Sugeno (1985) and Tong (1977). King and Mamdani (1977) and Kickert and van Nauta Lemke (1976) describe typical applications.

The three basic elements of a simple heuristic controller are shown in Figure 13.4. The first element "fuzzifies" any conventional measurements. A conventional measurement value is known as a singleton, that is, it has a single value. This must be assigned membership function values for each of the fuzzy reference sets for that measurement, which is simply done, as shown in Figure 13.5. The measurement 34°C has membership values (0.0, 0.0, 0.04, 0.95, 0.32) in the five reference fuzzy sets (very low, low, ok, high, very high). These numeric values make up the input possibility vector *Y*.

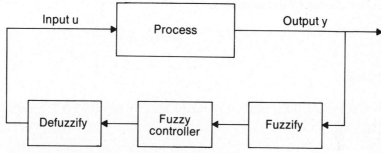

Figure 13.4 Fuzzy control components

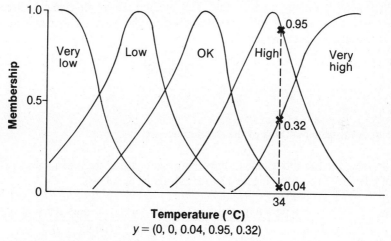

y = (0, 0, 0.04, 0.95, 0.32)

Figure 13.5 Fuzzification

The second element is the actual fuzzy control algorithm or rule set. The rule set can be precompiled into a fuzzy relation matrix. An output possibility vector can be calculated given the relation matrix and an input possibility vector. For example, a single-input, single-output controller could have the relation matrix:

$$R = \begin{bmatrix} 1.0 & 0.7 & 0.3 & 0.0 & 0.0 \\ 0.7 & 1.0 & 0.7 & 0.3 & 0.0 \\ 0.3 & 0.7 & 1.0 & 0.7 & 0.3 \\ 0.0 & 0.3 & 0.7 & 1.0 & 0.7 \\ 0.0 & 0.0 & 0.3 & 0.7 & 1.0 \end{bmatrix}$$

where the output also has five reference fuzzy sets, such as (very small, small, medium, large, very large).

Then the output possibility vector U would be (0.04, 0.30, 0.70, 0.95, 0.70), whose elements are defined by the relation:

$$u_i = \underset{j}{\max} \ \min (y_j, R_{ji})$$

For example:

$$u_3 = \max \left[\min(0, 0.3), \min(0, 0.7), \min(0.04, 1.0), \min(0.95, 0.7), \min(0.32, 0.3) \right]$$

$$u_3 = 0.7$$

The purpose of the third element, a "defuzzifier", is to extract a quantitative value from the fuzzy output which is then used as the control signal. The center-of-area (COA) method is usually used for this. This method selects the element corresponding to the center of area under the curve described by the fuzzy set membership function. Mathematically this is expressed as:

$$u_c = \frac{\sum_i u_i m_i}{\sum_i u_i}$$

where m_i is the center-of-area of the ith reference set.

The value for the above output possibility vector using the mean values of u for the output reference fuzzy sets (Figure 13.6) is calculated as follows:

$$u_c = \frac{0.04 * 0.0 + 0.3 * 2.5 + 0.7 * 5.0 + 0.95 * 7.5 + 0.7 * 10.0}{0.04 + 0.3 + 0.7 + 0.95 + 0.7}$$

$$u_c = 6.8$$

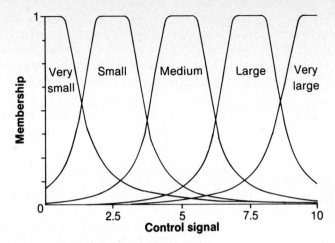

Figure 13.6 Output reference sets

13.4 Design procedure

The design procedure is as follows:

1. Define reference fuzzy sets for the inputs and outputs involved. The number of reference sets is an important design parameter. Too few sets result in relatively coarse control, while too many increases the number of control rules and the dimension of the relation matrix. The shape and location of the reference sets also has a significant effect on the controller performance, but at present there are no available guidelines for their positioning.
2. Define a set of control rules. These may be derived from the experience of operators and engineers who run the process. It is generally the most difficult step, and it is particularly difficult to ensure a "complete" rule set (a rule for all situations) and one without contradictions between rules regarding control action.
3. Compile the rules into a relation matrix. Simple rules of the type *If y is A then u is B*, where *A* and *B* are reference fuzzy sets, are simply *unity* in the appropriate positions in the relation matrix with zeros in the remaining positions.
4. Implement and test the controller.

In some situations it may be possible with some experience to bypass step 2 and directly define a relation matrix.

13.5 Application to the evaporator

As an elementary example of a fuzzy hierarchical controller, the product concentration $X2$ will be controlled by steam pressure $P100$. The pressure loop $P2$–$F200$ and the level loop $L2$–$F2$ will use PI controllers as in previous chapters with the same parameters.

   The input to the fuzzy controller will be $X2$ error (defined for this chapter as measurement minus setpoint) and the output will be a change in pressure $P100$. The use of the error signal allows the controller to react to both disturbances and setpoint changes without redefinition of rules or reference sets. Use of the change in the control action assists in minimizing offset by applying a type of integral control.

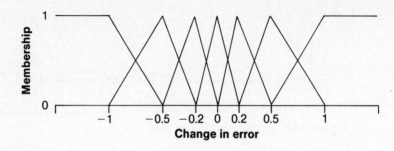

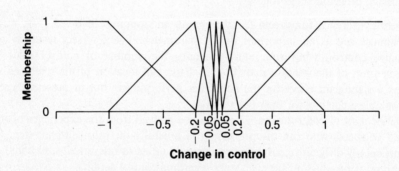

Figure 13.7 Fuzzy set definitions

   For both $X2$ error and the change in $P100$, five reference fuzzy sets were defined (see Figure 13.7) and called "Neg-big", "Neg-small", "None", "Pos-small" and "Pos-big". The width of the set "None" for the $X2$ error is a compromise between keeping the offset small and increasing the stability of the responses. The rule set was simply:

If error is Neg-big	*then* change is Pos-big
If error is Neg-small	*then* change is Pos-small
If error is None	*then* change is None
If error is Pos-small	*then* change is Neg-small
If error is Pos-big	*then* change is Neg-big

These result in a relation matrix with 1.0 on the diagonal from Row 1 Column 5 to Row 5 Column 1 and otherwise zero. The results of fuzzy heuristic control and PI control for a 10 percent decrease in feed flowrate $F1$ are compared in Figures 13.8 and 13.9 respectively. The heuristic controller is more stable but shows a small positive offset not visible in the figure. If the width of the "None" reference set for $X2$ error is decreased, the offset is reduced but the response becomes more oscillatory.

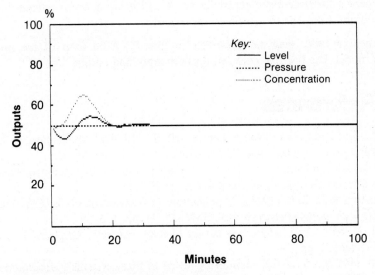

Figure 13.8 Fuzzy heuristic control

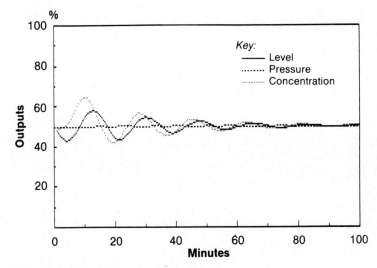

Figure 13.9 Conventional feedback control

13.6 Exercises

1. Implement a fuzzy heuristic controller on the $X2-P100$ loop of the nonlinear evaporator model. Use five reference sets for both input and output.

2. Quantitatively investigate the effect of the width of the "None" reference set for $X2$ error on the offset and stability of $X2$ responses to disturbances in $F1$ and $X1$.

3. Implement a fuzzy heuristic controller on $X2-P100$ using seven reference sets for input and output. Compare the results to those above.

4. Implement a fuzzy heuristic controller on the $P2-F200$ loop of the nonlinear evaporator model. Use five reference sets for both input and output.

13.7 References

Kickert, W. J. M. and Van Nauta Lemke, H. R. (1976), "Application of a fuzzy controller in a warm water plant", *Automatica*, Vol. 12, pp. 301–8.

King, P. J. and Mamdani, E. H. (1977), "The application of fuzzy control systems to industrial processes", *Automatica*, Vol. 13, pp. 235–42.

Maiers, J. and Sherif, Y. S. (1985), "Applications of fuzzy set theory", *IEEE Trans. on Systems, Man, and Cybernetics*, Vol. SMC-15 (1), pp. 175–89.

Sugeno, M. (1985), "An introductory survey of fuzzy control", *Information Sciences*, Vol. 36 (1 and 2), pp. 59–84.

Tong, R. M. (1977), "A control engineering review of fuzzy systems", *Automatica*, Vol. 13, pp. 559–69.

Zadeh, L. A. (1965), "Fuzzy sets", *Information and Control*, Vol. 8, pp. 338–53.

14 Fuzzy model based control

14.1 Introduction

One of the difficulties with fuzzy heuristic controllers, which were discussed in Chapter 13, is determining the control rules, or controller relation matrix. In many cases plant operators find it difficult to write down or verbalize the control rules that they use for operating the plant. In these instances, fuzzy model based control is best used. Of course the first problem with any model based control is determining the model. Often operators and plant engineers can more easily write down rules describing a plant model from their experience or knowledge of "first principles", for example "*If* cooling water is increased *then* reactor temperature drops". Another approach is to use recently developed fuzzy identification algorithms (Graham and Newell 1988). A combination of the two model building approaches may also be of advantage.

14.2 Fuzzy model identification

This chapter will present an algorithm for identifying a relation matrix in the form of a first-order, single-input, single-output model from process input-output data. The model is of the general form:

$$Y_k = Y_{k-1} \circ U_{k-d} \circ R \qquad (14.1)$$

where Y and U are possibility vectors for model output and input respectively and R is the model relation matrix (see Chapter 13 Sections 13.2 and 13.3 for definitions). Subscript k represents current time, $k - 1$ one sampling time in the past and $k - d$ the deadtime of d sampling periods in the past.

The identification procedure is then as follows:

1. Select the model form (Equation 14.1 above in this case) and the process deadtime d.

2. Select appropriate sets of fuzzy reference sets for the input and output (e.g. those in Figure 13.7).
3. Collect appropriate input-output data from the process (refer to Chapter 3 Section 3.2).
4. Apply the identification algorithm described below to evaluate the model relation matrix (using N reference sets for each variable gives a $N \times N \times N$ relation matrix).

The identification algorithm is as follows:

1. Take an initial relation matrix R. This may be empty or may include operator/ engineer knowledge as a starting point.
2. Take a set of data y_k, y_{k-1} and u_{k-d}.
3. Fuzzify the data to obtain the possibility vectors Y_k, Y_{k-1} and U_{k-d}.
4. Evaluate a relation matrix:

$$R' = U_{k-d} \times Y_{k-1} \times Y_k$$

5. Determine $i*$ and $j*$ denoting the positions of the maximum membership values in the possibility vectors U_k and Y_{k-1} respectively.
6. Use the following to update R from R':

$$R(i*, j*, k) = a \cdot R'(i*, j*, k) + (1 - a) \cdot R(i*, j*, k) \qquad k = 1, N$$

$$R(i, j, k) = \max (R'(i, j, k), R(i, j, k)) \text{ for all } i, j, k \text{ except } i = i*, j = j*$$

where a is a scalar constant between 0.5 (good noise rejection) and 1.0 (fastest update).
7. Return to Step 2 if there is more data.

More details on the algorithm and underlying information can be found in Graham (1987) and Graham and Newell (1988).

14.3 Fuzzy identification on the evaporator

The above procedure was used to develop a fuzzy model for the effect of steam pressure $P100$ on product concentration $X2$. The standard PI control loops were used for separator level $L2$ and operating pressure $P2$.

The reference sets in Figure 13.7 and the scaling factors 30.0 and 60.0 were used for $X2$ and $P100$ deviation variables (from steady state) respectively.

Data was generated by applying a change to $P100$ every 15 minutes. The deviations from steady state of $P100$ were uniformly, randomly distributed between $+60$ kPa and -60 kPa. Five thousand data points were collected at one minute intervals.

The resulting relation matrix is listed in Appendix E. Figure 14.1 compares the nonlinear model and the fuzzy model for a different series of disturbances to $P100$. Reasonable agreement is obtained.

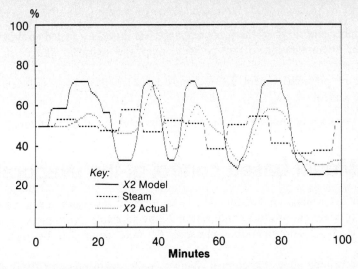

Figure 14.1 Response of fuzzy model to steam changes

14.4 Fuzzy model based control

The general structure of a fuzzy model based controller is shown in Figure 14.2. There is a fixed set of possible control actions from which to choose, for example, a number of positive and negative changes.

The model is used to predict what the output would be for each of these actions. The decision maker then selects the most favorable action to take, for example, the one which results in the smallest error. The selected control action is then applied to the process and the whole procedure repeats itself each control interval.

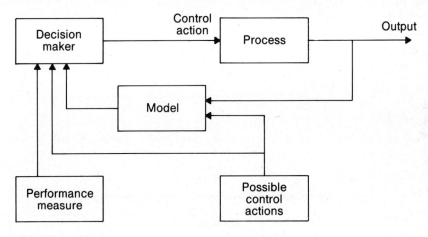

Figure 14.2 Fuzzy model based controller

There are two factors which require careful engineering:

1. The number and range of the fuzzy reference sets must be selected so that the model is a fair representation of the process over the expected range of operating conditions.
2. The set of possible control actions must be selected to give sufficient, yet fine enough, control.

There are as yet no guidelines to assist with the selection of these factors.

14.5 Model based control of the evaporator

The model determined in Section 14.3 was used as the basis for a model based controller, to maintain product composition $X2$ by adjusting steam pressure $P100$. The separator level $L2$ and operating pressure $P2$ were controlled by their usual PI controllers.

There were nine allowable control changes in the steam pressure $P100$: 0.0, ±0.5, ±1.0, ±4.0 and ±7.0 kPa. These were added in turn to the current value of $P100$ and fed to the model together with the current value of $X2$. The model calculated the expected value of $X2$ at the next control interval. The change in $P100$ that resulted in the smallest absolute error in $X2$ was chosen as the control action to be applied to the process.

The response of the nonlinear model of the evaporator to a 10 percent decrease in feed flowrate $F1$, with PI and fuzzy model based control, is shown in Figure 14.3. The response with a standard PI controller on $X2$ is shown in Figure 14.4. The model based controller gives a smaller deviation and more stable response, but with a small negative offset. Other load disturbances can result in larger offsets of up to 3 percent.

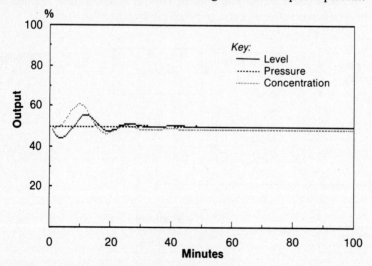

Figure 14.3 Fuzzy model based control

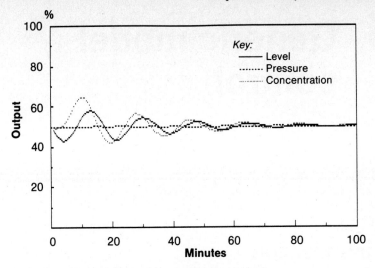

Figure 14.4 Conventional feedback control

The offsets result from the wide range and small number of fuzzy reference sets used in the controller. The wide range was necessary to cover the expected range of operating conditions caused by disturbances. Because the number of reference sets was small, the central reference set covered 0.2 × 30.0 or 6 percent each side of the set value of 25 percent. The offsets obtained fell well within the central reference set and were therefore essentially ignored by the controller. To reduce the offsets a larger number of reference sets would have to be defined.

14.6 Exercises

1. Develop a fuzzy model for the effect of cooling water flowrate $F200$ on the operating pressure $P2$. Use a similar form of model and the same reference sets as above.

2. Using the model obtained in exercise 1, implement and test a fuzzy model based controller, in place of the PI loop controlling operating pressure $P2$ by adjusting cooling water flowrate $F200$.

14.7 References

Graham, B. P. (1987), "Fuzzy Identification and Control", Ph.D. thesis, University of Queensland, Australia.

Graham, B. P. and Newell, R. B. (1988), "Fuzzy Identification and Control of a Liquid Level Rig", *Fuzzy Sets and Systems*, Vol. 26, No. 3, pp. 255–73.

15 Generic model control

15.1 Introduction

Since the beginning of the 1980s, there has been an increased interest in multivariable control techniques. This has been illustrated by the work on Dynamic Matrix Control (DMC) (Cutler 1983), Model Algorithmic Control (MAC) (Richalet, Rault, Testud and Papon 1979), and Internal Model Control (IMC) (Garcia and Morari 1982). These techniques are all similar in the sense that they rely on models to predict the behavior of the process over some future time interval, and the control calculations are based on these model predictions. The models used for these predictions have usually been linear approximations of the process or experimentally obtained step response data. Unfortunately, real chemical processes generally behave in a quite nonlinear manner, and some chemical and biochemical processes change behavior over a period of time. For these processes, the linear model predictions are not a good approximation and it is important to seek other methods that yield high performance control strategies. The single effect, forced circulation evaporator is indeed such a process.

Recently, Lee and Sullivan (1988) presented a generalized method to employ a nonlinear process model directly in a control strategy, Generic Model Control (GMC). The work described is based on the principle of using the best available process model as the means of developing a control strategy. This process model is derived from fundamental conservation and constitutive relations. This type of model will fully describe the process nonlinearities and interactions that occur between process variables.

15.2 GMC applied to the evaporator

The overall structure of GMC allows the incorporation of nonlinear process models directly into the control algorithm. A brief description of this method and its application to the evaporator is given below.

Consider a process described by the following equation:

$$\frac{d\underset{\sim}{x}}{dt} = \underset{\sim}{f}(\underset{\sim}{x}, \underset{\sim}{u}, \underset{\sim}{d}) \tag{15.1}$$

where: $\underset{\sim}{x}$ is the state vector of dimension n.

$\underset{\sim}{u}$ is the vector of manipulated variables of dimension n.

$\underset{\sim}{d}$ is the vector of disturbance variables dimension l.

The more general case, when the state vector $\underset{\sim}{x}$ and the control vector $\underset{\sim}{u}$ do not have the same dimension, is presented by Lee and Sullivan (1988). In general, $\underset{\sim}{f}$ is some nonlinear function.

When the process is away from its desired steady state $\underset{\sim}{x}^*$ we would like the rate of change of $\underset{\sim}{x}$, $(d\underset{\sim}{x}/dt)^*$, to be such that the process is returning towards steady state, that is:

$$\left(\frac{d\underset{\sim}{x}}{dt}\right)^* = \underset{\sim}{K}_1(\underset{\sim}{x}^* - \underset{\sim}{x}) \tag{15.2}$$

where: $\underset{\sim}{K}_1$ is a diagonal matrix.

In addition, we would like the process to have zero offset, that is:

$$\left(\frac{d\underset{\sim}{x}}{dt}\right)^* = \underset{\sim}{K}_2 \int (\underset{\sim}{x}^* - \underset{\sim}{x})\, dt \tag{15.3}$$

where: $\underset{\sim}{K}_2$ is a diagonal matrix.

Good control performance will be given by some combination of these objectives, that is:

$$\left(\frac{d\underset{\sim}{x}}{dt}\right)^* = \underset{\sim}{K}_1(\underset{\sim}{x}^* - \underset{\sim}{x}) + \underset{\sim}{K}_2 \int (\underset{\sim}{x}^* - \underset{\sim}{x})\, dt \tag{15.4}$$

It can be shown that $\underset{\sim}{K}_1$ and $\underset{\sim}{K}_2$ in Equation 15.4 will result in a performance specification for $\underset{\sim}{x}(t)$. By definition, good control can be obtained when $d\underset{\sim}{x}/dt$ follows $(d\underset{\sim}{x}/dt)^*$. Equating equation 15.1 and equation 15.4 and rearranging yields:

$$\underset{\sim}{f}(\underset{\sim}{x}, \underset{\sim}{u}, \underset{\sim}{d}) - \underset{\sim}{K}_1(\underset{\sim}{x}^* - \underset{\sim}{x}) - \underset{\sim}{K}_2 \int (\underset{\sim}{x}^* - \underset{\sim}{x})\, dt = 0 \tag{15.5}$$

The solution of Equation 15.5 for $\underset{\sim}{u}$ will yield a control law that tracks the desired performance of $\underset{\sim}{x}(t)$, if $\underset{\sim}{u}$ is not constrained.

In general, the exact process model is rarely known, and an approximate model is introduced such that:

$$\hat{\underset{\sim}{f}}(\underset{\sim}{x}, \underset{\sim}{u}, \underset{\sim}{d}) - \underset{\sim}{K}_1(\underset{\sim}{x}^* - \underset{\sim}{x}) - \underset{\sim}{K}_2 \int (\underset{\sim}{x}^* - \underset{\sim}{x})\, dt = \underset{\sim}{0} \tag{15.6}$$

where $\hat{\underset{\sim}{f}}$ represents the approximation to the true model.

Any inaccuracies introduced by this approximation will be compensated by the integral term in the control algorithm. This is similar in nature to IMC (Garcia and Morari 1982) which can be considered to be an integral-only controller on the plant-model mismatch, and a general model prediction of the non-minimum phase components of the plant. This integral term in the control law ensures that the controller is robust despite modeling errors.

Applying this control law to the evaporator, and assuming that f is equal to the right hand sides of Equations 2.1, 2.2 and 2.3 of Chapter 2, yields the following set of control equations:

$$F2 = \frac{F1\ X1}{X2*} - \frac{1}{X2*}(Mk_{11}(X2* - X2) + Mk_{12} \int (X2* - X2)\,dt) \quad (15.7)$$

$$Q100 = \lambda(F1 - F2) + F1\ C_p(T2 - T1) - \rho A\lambda(k_{21}(L2* - L2) + k_{22} \int (L2* - L2)\,dt) \quad (15.8)$$

$$Q200 = Q100 - F1\ C_p(T2 - T1) - C\lambda(k_{31}(P2* - P2) + k_{32} \int (P2* - P2)\,dt) \quad (15.9)$$

where: k_{ij} is the ith diagonal element of the matrix $\underset{\sim}{K}_j$.

$P100$ may be found by manipulation of Equations 2.4, 2.7, 2.8 and 15.8, while $F200$ may be found by manipulation of Equations 2.10 and 15.9:

$$P100 = (Q100/(0.16(F1 + F3)) + T2 - 90.0)/0.1538 \quad (15.10)$$

$$F200 = UA2\ Q200(2C_p(UA2(T3 - T200) - Q200)) \quad (15.11)$$

The choice of the matrices $\underset{\sim}{K}_1$ and $\underset{\sim}{K}_2$ influence the closed-loop response and as such may be considered as tuning parameters. Lee and Sullivan (1988) described how these parameters may be chosen in a systematic manner. For this process the following values were used:

$$k_{11} = 3.0 \times 10^{-2} \qquad k_{12} = 2.5 \times 10^{-5}$$
$$k_{21} = 0.6 \qquad k_{22} = 4.0 \times 10^{-2}$$
$$k_{31} = 6.0 \times 10^{-2} \qquad k_{32} = 1.0 \times 10^{-4}$$

Equations 15.7, 15.8 and 15.9 describe a controller that includes feedforward control action by the inclusion of $X1$, $F1$, and $T1$; decoupling control action through the process model; and of course, feedback action through the control performance specification. It is also interesting to note the pairing of control loops that this formulation has developed. The exit concentration $X2$ is controlled by manipulating the exit flowrate $F2$; the level in the separator $L2$ is controlled by manipulating the steam pressure $P100$, but with interaction decoupling from $F2$; and the pressure in the evaporator $P2$ is controlled by manipulating the cooling water flowrate $F200$ but, again, with interaction decoupling from both $F2$ and $P100$.

A control strategy based on maintaining inventories within the system as described in Chapter 4 would have reversed the pairing of the first two loops while retaining the structure of the final loop. Such a structure would not of course include any decoupling control action. Hence, one of the advantages of the GMC formulation is the possible determination of the optimal control structure in order to minimize interactions.

15.3 Control performance

In Cases 1 to 5 described below, the disturbance consisted of a decrease in the feed flowrate. The results from this disturbance are indicative of the behavior of the controllers to many other disturbances. Quantification of the results is shown in Table 15.1 and will be discussed after the different control cases are described.

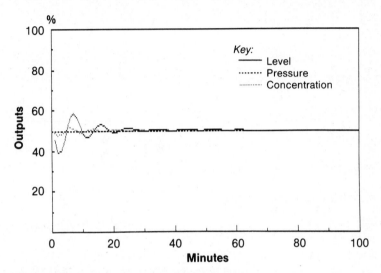

Figure 15.1 Full generic model control

Case 1—Full model based control

The full control strategy as described in Equations 15.7, 15.8 and 15.9 was tested for a 25 percent decrease in $F1$ and the result is shown in Figure 15.1. As can be seen, the regulation performance is extremely good. The manipulated variables also respond smoothly to this disturbance and settle to the final values quickly.

Case 2—No feedforward action

The result shown in Figure 15.1 assumes that measurements of the inlet disturbances are available, thus enabling feedforward action in the control law. If these measurements were not available, the appropriate terms ($F1$, $X1$ and $T1$) in the model could be set to some nominal steady-state values as shown in Table 2.1 in Chapter 2. The result for a controller employing this strategy for the same disturbance is shown in Figure 15.2. It can be seen that the control movement is slightly slower and has some small offset without feedforward action, but does not significantly affect the performance. These results are directly comparable to the results obtained using PI control (Case 4) and Predictive Control (Case 5) described below. Neither of these cases include feedforward control action. The small offsets could be removed by choosing different values of the tuning parameters—specifically increasing the integral terms.

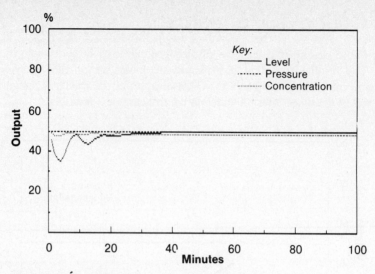

Figure 15.2 GMC without feedforward terms

Case 3—Model simplifications

The sensible heat terms ($F1\ C_p\ (T2 - T1)$) in the energy balances represent only approximately 10 percent of the energy transferred. Thus it would seem reasonable to neglect these terms in the control algorithm. In addition, no feedforward action was included as Case 2 had shown that good performance was achievable without this component of the control law. The result of using this strategy is shown in Figure 15.3. It can be seen that compared to the full model based control (Figure 15.1), the control response is degraded. Comparing the results shown in Figures 15.2 and 15.3, it appears

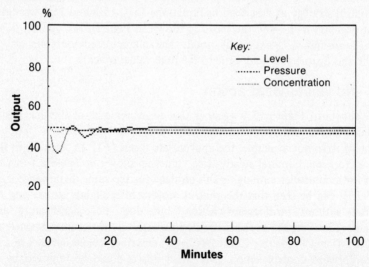

Figure 15.3 GMC without feedforward or sensible heat terms

that the model structure (i.e. including the sensible heat terms) is more important than the absolute numerical values.

Case 4—Inventory control

As discussed in the previous section, a control strategy employing PI controllers to maintain the mass and energy inventories in the process would result in a different pairing of the controlled and manipulated variables. The pairing used for PI control was outlined in Chapter 4 and consisted of *L2–F2*, *P2–F200*, and *X2–P100*.

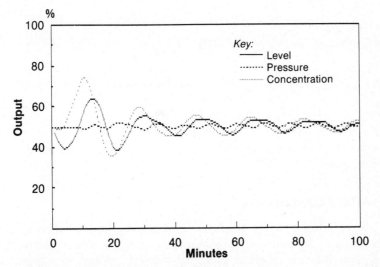

Figure 15.4 Conventional feedback control

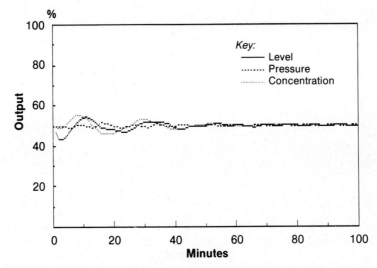

Figure 15.5 Conventional feedforward–feedback control

Each loop was tuned using the methods as described in Chapter 4. The controllers were considerably detuned to achieve stable operation when all loops were running in automatic mode together. The result of using such a strategy is shown in Figure 15.4 without feedforward action from $F1$ and in Figure 15.5 with feedforward action. The disturbance in this case was only a 15 percent decrease in $F1$; the larger disturbance used previously resulted in an unstable response. It can be seen that the result is not nearly as good as model based control strategies. In fact, it can be shown that simple PI control results from GMC if we choose $\hat{f}$ according to:

$$\frac{dL2}{dt} = F2$$

$$\frac{dP2}{dt} = F200$$

and:

$$\frac{dX2}{dt} = P100$$

The structure of $\hat{f}$ differs so markedly from f, one cannot expect good control performance.

Case 5—Predictive control

As discussed in the introduction, predictive control has gained considerable popularity during this decade. To compare the performance of GMC with predictive control, a predictive controller was designed using the method outlined in Chapter 11. The controller used as controlled outputs, the evaporator pressure $P2$ and the exit

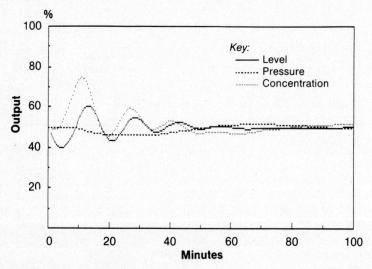

Figure 15.6 Predictive control

concentration $X2$ and used the steam supply pressure $P100$ and the cooling water flowrate $F200$, as the manipulated variables. The separator level $L2$ was controlled using the exit flowrate $F2$ as a manipulated variable. This controller was implemented with a PI algorithm, making the remaining part of the process open-loop bounded. This overall control structure thus does not contain feedforward action and the result of using this controller is shown in Figure 15.6. The behavior of the predictive controller is not as good as those obtained using the model based controllers of Cases 1, 2 and 3. This is because the model based controllers more accurately model the nonlinear behavior of the system than the simple linear step response model imbedded in the predictive controller structure.

Quantitative analysis

A quantitative analysis of the control performance for the different controllers is presented in Table 15.1. The results in this table represent the integral of the absolute error multiplied by time (ITAE) for the error in each controlled variable. It can be seen that the full model-based control clearly out-performs all other controllers. The model-based control without feedforward control action is markedly better than the other feedback-only strategies (Inventory PI loops and predictive control).

Table 15.1 *ITAE results*

	$X2$ (%.mins)	$P2$ (kPa.mins)	$L2$ (m.mins)
Full GMC	90.0	207.0	20.0
GMC—No feedforward	1070.0	551.0	330.0
GMC—No sensible heat	1090.0	6990.0	165.0
PI Inventory Control	13500.0	7200.0	436.0
Predictive Control	6600.0	7900.0	127.0

15.4 Exercise

Further examine the performance of the full model based controller using two other disturbances: a 20 percent increase in all set-points simultaneously; and the response to a 25 percent increase in the feed concentration.

Acknowledgements

The authors would like to thank Professor Gerry Sullivan at the University of Waterloo, Canada, for his help in the preparation of this chapter.

15.5 References

Cutler, C. R. (1983), "Dynamic matrix control: An optimal multivariable algorithm with constraints", Ph.D. thesis, Univ. of Houston.

Garcia, C. E. and Morari, M. (1982), "Internal model control 1: A unifying review and some new results", *Ind Eng Chem Proc Des Dev*, Vol. 21, pp. 308–23.

Lee, P. L. and Sullivan, G. R. (1988), "Generic Model Control: Theory and Applications", International Federation of Automatic Control Workshop on Process Model Based Control, Atlanta, Georgia, USA, June 13–14.

Richalet, J., Rault, A., Testud, J. L. and Papon, J. (1979), "Model predictive heuristic control: Applications to industrial processes", *Automatica*, Vol. 14, pp. 413–28.

Appendix A:
Software catalog

A number of simulations of the nonlinear evaporator model have been developed. The most extensively developed suite of computer programs that support this book is described in more detail in section A.1. In addition a number of computer-based simulations have been developed. A short description of each, together with its availability is given in Section A.2.

A.1 PC software

The many control strategies described in the main body of the book were developed with the aid of software available directly from Prentice Hall. This software was also used to generate all of the plots contained in this book. The software is menu-driven, it allows the student to interactively change many of the control system design or tuning parameters and is a convenient way for students to complete many of the exercises contained in the book.

You may obtain a copy of the six discettes that contain this software by contacting:

Pat Walsh
Prentice Hall of Australia Pty Ltd
7 Grosvenor Place
Brookvale, New South Wales 2100

Tel (02) 939 1333

Charles Decker
Prentice Hall International Inc.
Englewood Cliffs, New Jersey 07632
USA

Tel (201) 592 2000

Jill Jones
Prentice Hall International (UK) Limited
66 Wood Lane End
Hemel Hempstead, Herts HP2 4RG
England

Tel 0011 44 442 212771

Gunawan Hadi
Prentice Hall of Southeast Asia Pty Ltd
24 Pasir Panjang Road
#04-31, PSA Multi Storey Complex
Singapore 0511

Tel (65) 278 9611

Available programs

The following programs and the corresponding discettes upon which they reside is shown below. This list shows the actual menu presented to the student when the software is run.

APPLIED PROCESS CONTROL — A CASE STUDY

Bob Newell and Peter Lee

SIMULATION PROGRAMS

1. Return to DOS

2. Step Tests	(Disc 1)	3. Fit Step Tests	(Disc 1)
4. Feedback Control	(Disc 1)	5. Feedforward Control	(Disc 1)
6. Decoupled Control	(Disc 1)	7. Deadtime Comp.	(Disc 1)
8. Multivariable Design	(Disc 3)	9. Multivariable Test	(Disc 3)
10. Contin. to Discrete	(Disc 4)	11. Con. & Obs. Check	(Disc 2)
12. Kalman Filter Design	(Disc 2)	13. Kalman Filter Test	(Disc 2)
14. Gain Scheduling	(Disc 3)	15. Self Tuning Reg.	(Disc 3)
16. Pred. Control Des.	(Disc 5)	17. Pred. Control Test	(Disc 4)
18. Contraint Control	(Disc 3)	19. GMC Control	(Disc 4)
20. Fuzzy Heuristic	(Disc 4)	21. Fuzzy Model	(Disc 4)

Hardware requirements

The minimum requirements for running the simulation programs are as follows:
- an IBM-compatible PC, PC-XT or PC-AT;
- a monochrome display on a CGA controller;
- an 8087 or 80287 coprocessor;
- two floppy disc drives or one and a hard disc;
- DOS 2.0 or higher.

Installing the software

1. Make a working copy of the distribution discs (DISKCOPY may be used—the discs are not copy protected). Add to the working copy of the MASTER DISC a copy of COMMAND.EXE.
2. On a dual floppy system the discs can be used as is:
   (a) Place the MASTER disc in drive A: (which must be the default drive).
   (b) Place one of DISC ONE to DISC FIVE in drive B:.
   (c) Type the command RUN.
   (d) Select the appropriate menu numbers.
   (e) Press the RETURN (ENTER) key to proceed from the plots.
   For the first simulation selected, or if the disk in drive B: does not have the requested simulation program, the software will display the message "Not found—Enter Drive:". Place the appropriate disc in drive B: and enter B.
3. On a hard disc system make an appropriately named subdirectory and copy into it the MASTER DISC and as many of the DISC ONE to DISC FIVE as you wish. To speed up execution while not using too much hard disc space, the DISC ONE to DISC FIVE could be used in a floppy drive with only the MASTER DISC contents on the hard disc.
   (a) Make the subdirectory the default directory.
   (b) Type the command RUN.
   (c) Select the appropriate menu numbers.
   (d) Press the RETURN (ENTER) key to proceed from the plots.
   If the simulations are still on floppy you will be asked for the drive.

Saving simulation results

The simulation results can be copied to other files for safekeeping if the command RUN is replaced by RUN SAVE. The saved files are called PLOT.nnn and the corresponding parameters are called PARAM.nnn where nnn = 101 to 999 in the order in which the simulations are performed.

These files are created in the default directory and amount to about 11 kbytes per run. The MASTER DISC for a dual floppy configuration has room for only about 15 simulations.

Graphics hardcopy

There are two ways to obtain a hardcopy of the simulation plots:
1. Make sure you run the DOS program GRAPHICS before issuing the command RUN. When the appropriate plot is displayed press PrtSc to dump the plot on your printer.

2. Write your own plotting program and read the data from the tabular data files PLOT.DAT or PLOT.nnn. The format of these files is described below:

LINE 1:   N the number of data points.

LINE 2
to: seven columns of data usually consisting of
LINE N+1   TIME,$L2$,$X2$,$P2$,$F2$,$P100$,$F200$

LINE N+2
to: information for program GRAPHF.EXE
LINE M

A.2 Other software

In addition to the menu based PC software as described above, a number of simulations of the evaporator are available.

Available from the University of Queensland

1. A simulation of the evaporator using the dynamic simulation language SPEEDUP.
2. A simulation of the evaporator plus some (but not all) of the control schemes implemented on the IBM Advanced Control System (ACS).
3. A simulation of the evaporator implemented on a Bailey Network 90 Distributed Control System.
   Enquiries regarding the availability of this software should be sent directly to the authors:

Dr R. B. Newell or Dr P. L. Lee
Department of Chemical Engineering
University of Queensland
St. Lucia, Queensland 4067
Australia.

Tel. 61 7 377 2081
Fax 61 7 870 3848
Bitnet: newell@uqcspe.bitnet.oz

Available from SHIE Special Systems Pty Ltd

SHIE Special Systems market a very good Time Series Analysis (TSA) package which will run on IBM PCs or clones. The package is especially suited to the task of identifying dynamic models for control system design, and the authors used this package extensively in Chapter 3. Enquiries may be sent to:

SHIE Special Systems Pty Ltd
28 Fairley St
Indooroopilly, Queensland 4068
Australia.

Tel. 61 7 870 3205

Available from the University of Sydney

The Department of Chemical Engineering at the University of Sydney developed some teaching material based around a simulation of the evaporator model using a PC-based process control package called FIX. FIX is a commercial product of Intellution Inc., the address of which is given below. The University of Sydney material consists of a number of simulations for different control strategies and a set of student notes. The material may be obtained directly from:

Dr G. W. Barton
Department of Chemical Engineering
University of Sydney
New South Wales 2006
Australia.

Fax 61 2 692 2012

FIX may be obtained from:

Intellution Inc.
35 Perwal St
Westwood, Massachusetts 02090
USA

or,

METQUIP Pty Ltd
Centrecourt
25 Paul St
North Ryde, New South Wales 2114
Australia

Tel 61 2 805 0311
Fax 61 2 805 0136

Appendix B:
Elements of the evaporator Jacobians

```
AA(1,1) = 0.0
AA(1,2) = 9.33E-5*F1 + 6.49E-5*F3
AA(1,3) = 16.76E-5*F1 + 11.66E-5*F3
AA(2,1) = 0.0
AA(2,2) = -0.05*F2
AA(2,3) = 0.0
AA(3,1) = 0.0
AA(3,2) = -4.668E-4*F1 - 3.247E-4*F3
AA(3,3) = -8.152E-4*F1 - 5.670E-4*F3-2.252E-2*F200/(F200+48.86)
BB(1,1) = -0.05
BB(1,2) = -3.19E-5*(F1+F3)
BB(1,3) = 0.0
BB(2,1) = -0.05*X2
BB(2,2) = 0.0
BB(2,3) = 0.0
BB(3,1) = 0.0
BB(3,2) = 1.597E-4*(F1+F3)
BB(3,3) = -0.0444*(.507*P2 + 55. - T200)*48.86/(F200+48.86)**2
DD(1,1) = -2.077E-4*(.1538*P100 + 90. - .5616*P2 - .3126*X2 - 48.43)
DD(1,2) = 0.05*(1 - 4.156E-3*(.1538*P100 + 90. - .5616*P2
*       - .3126*X2 - 48.43) - 1.818E-3*(.5616*P2 + .3126*X2
*       + 48.43 - T1))
DD(1,3) = 0.0
DD(1,4) = -9.09E-5*F1
DD(1,5) = 0.0
DD(2,1) = 0.0
DD(2,2) = 0.05*X1
DD(2,3) = 0.05*F1
DD(2,4) = 0.0
DD(2,5) = 0.0
```

```
  DD(3,1) = 1.039E-3*(.1538*P100 + 90. - .5616*P2 - .3126*X2 - 48.43)
  DD(3,2) = 1.039E-3*(.1538*P100 + 90. - .5616*P2 - .3126*X2
*        - 48.43) - 4.545E-4*(.5616*P2 + .3216*X2 + 48.43 - T1)
  DD(3,3) = 0.0
  DD(3,4) = 4.545E-4*F1
  DD(3,5) = .0444*F200/(F200+48.86)
```

Appendix C:
Evaporator time series data

Time	P100	X2	Time	P100	X2	Time	P100	X2
1	191.33	24.50	25	163.88	21.06	49	204.92	31.48
2	193.48	24.42	26	170.40	18.97	50	196.23	32.14
3	202.31	24.13	27	178.81	17.96	51	190.10	32.21
4	208.36	24.90	28	185.70	17.34	52	189.16	31.60
5	212.37	24.99	29	188.25	17.20	53	191.02	30.29
6	210.06	25.33	30	184.88	17.53	54	192.72	28.07
7	206.01	25.90	31	182.20	19.18	55	191.60	26.95
8	202.37	27.11	32	179.47	21.04	56	192.03	25.71
9	203.70	27.64	33	178.65	22.61	57	192.41	24.69
10	202.99	28.37	34	182.49	24.42	58	193.85	23.65
11	196.79	29.30	35	187.48	24.63	59	194.56	24.24
12	194.01	29.82	36	192.55	24.63	60	189.63	25.09
13	199.72	29.53	37	197.87	24.08	61	185.24	26.38
14	199.53	29.20	38	200.63	23.17	62	182.20	27.40
15	201.70	28.82	39	201.73	22.42	63	180.70	27.73
16	202.10	28.69	40	205.81	21.99	64	182.13	26.69
17	197.79	28.33	41	210.93	21.99	65	188.30	25.10
18	189.04	28.06	42	215.78	22.37	66	198.74	23.67
19	180.32	27.59	43	220.21	22.52	67	201.80	21.57
20	173.84	26.70	44	222.00	23.00	68	204.22	19.12
21	167.63	26.69	45	225.35	23.89	69	204.13	17.33
22	161.58	25.75	46	228.12	25.34	70	199.92	16.15
23	159.05	23.97	47	225.96	26.93	71	196.11	16.38
24	160.63	23.05	48	217.74	29.22	72	196.07	17.53

Time	P100	X2	Time	P100	X2	Time	P100	X2
73	191.86	19.18	124	197.98	33.84	175	177.34	23.60
74	187.47	20.95	125	202.04	35.11	176	178.81	22.72
75	186.35	23.82	126	206.85	34.62	177	184.27	21.66
76	182.43	26.02	127	213.08	33.02	178	196.14	20.65
77	177.81	27.47	128	218.46	30.30	179	203.88	20.89
78	173.32	27.44	129	217.63	27.64	180	213.65	21.40
79	170.93	26.99	130	211.51	25.36	181	220.42	22.78
80	174.00	25.88	131	206.45	24.64	182	222.83	23.84
81	174.33	24.48	132	204.07	24.44	183	221.38	25.28
82	171.77	22.88	133	200.42	25.46	184	220.35	27.11
83	165.26	20.74	134	195.23	26.87	185	218.37	29.40
84	159.86	18.47	135	188.42	28.31	186	211.91	31.72
85	159.71	17.33	136	183.57	28.93	187	205.93	33.93
86	163.28	17.52	137	185.04	28.65	188	202.95	35.02
87	164.40	18.68	138	190.62	27.56	189	199.23	35.07
88	169.72	20.42	139	199.22	25.83	190	197.79	34.15
89	179.49	21.15	140	205.56	23.47	191	202.58	32.69
90	187.29	21.38	141	213.35	21.92	192	209.71	30.22
91	193.11	21.59	142	219.42	21.39	193	213.35	28.25
92	198.84	21.27	143	222.50	21.76	194	209.27	25.92
93	200.68	20.31	144	228.45	23.18	195	203.28	23.62
94	204.70	19.73	145	230.23	25.17	196	202.79	21.95
95	203.28	19.93	146	229.70	26.54	197	204.28	21.74
96	201.73	21.50	147	226.78	27.03	198	207.58	24.06
97	202.13	23.78	148	219.81	27.31	199	208.85	26.43
98	204.68	26.07	149	210.26	28.38	200	204.07	28.73
99	206.38	27.89	150	202.17	29.64	201	198.95	30.98
100	207.52	28.92	151	196.36	31.09	202	192.41	32.68
101	208.54	28.91	152	192.54	31.66	203	181.84	33.43
102	203.77	28.50	153	195.74	30.75	204	712.60	33.08
103	192.25	28.31	154	201.22	29.06	205	167.06	31.69
104	178.76	28.73	155	206.89	26.09	206	163.63	29.46
105	168.37	29.00	156	209.86	23.53	207	164.18	26.74
106	162.06	28.59	157	205.34	21.48	208	169.08	24.80
107	158.31	26.86	158	192.67	20.93	209	170.71	23.43
108	154.27	25.21	159	181.35	20.80	210	176.84	22.69
109	154.66	23.55	160	171.13	22.21	211	183.52	21.44
110	160.12	21.27	161	168.49	23.87	212	185.01	20.60
111	162.51	18.91	162	173.16	25.64	213	190.22	20.72
112	167.35	17.31	163	179.79	27.09	214	190.42	22.21
113	179.60	15.97	164	189.17	27.63	215	192.36	23.28
114	196.70	15.83	165	195.80	26.98	216	197.27	23.70
115	211.00	15.67	166	197.24	25.80	217	202.84	24.52
116	223.64	16.39	167	198.76	24.19	218	212.15	25.83
117	223.92	17.17	168	195.87	22.86	219	216.74	27.23
118	217.80	17.75	169	191.03	22.44	220	217.74	28.79
119	213.72	19.33	170	187.27	22.63	221	213.85	29.34
120	207.69	21.33	171	179.13	23.16	222	207.96	29.86
121	204.64	23.91	172	176.15	23.71	223	198.69	29.80
122	199.05	26.60	173	176.70	24.24	224	190.65	29.41
123	197.97	30.37	174	175.91	24.39	225	185.02	29.84

Time	P100	X2	Time	P100	X2	Time	P100	X2
226	180.12	29.71	235	202.49	25.34	244	191.52	25.33
227	177.41	28.84	236	204.02	25.70	245	192.75	25.90
228	178.96	28.26	237	200.69	25.88	246	199.66	26.20
229	189.21	26.77	238	198.96	26.35	247	201.79	25.94
230	200.13	25.14	239	200.64	26.89	248	202.11	25.68
231	205.49	23.31	240	203.54	27.08	249	199.41	25.43
232	206.97	22.66	241	204.90	26.86	250	192.92	25.71
233	205.18	23.46	242	203.70	25.91			
234	203.54	24.26	243	195.45	25.54			

Appendix D:

Inventory control of process plants — An application of control system synthesis

Introduction

This Appendix addresses the question of how to design a control system to maintain steady mass and energy inventories in a process plant. Only single-loop control strategies are considered, as these are still the predominant form of control used in the processing industries. A systematic approach based on qualitative dynamic mass and energy balances is used to develop an integrated control system. An example of this approach is also presented.

The control of process plants is carried out to satisfy three objectives:
1. The maintenance of safe operation;
2. The maintenance of steady operation;
3. The maintenance of optimal operating conditions.

These objectives must be met despite the effects of often frequent and large processing disturbances.

The first objective (safe operation) is frequently satisfied by the addition of specific "control" systems such as alarm and trip systems. The third objective (optimal operation) is usually satisfied by the application of scheduling and optimising methods, both off-line and on-line.

Conventional single-loop control loop systems are generally aimed at satisfying the second objective, that of maintaining steady operation. Maintaining steady operation implies that good control of the mass and energy inventories within the plant has been achieved. It is this topic that this Appendix seeks to address. The theory and "art" of control system synthesis has recently been reviewed by Stephanopoulos (1983). Nearly all the previous work has only considered steady-state information. This ignores important dynamic transients that "upset" process operation.

The approach described here aims at using dynamic information to derive a control system design which will maintain stable inventory control. The design produced is not claimed to be "optimal" or the best possible. It only considers single-loop feedback control loops. Experienced practitioners could always modify the designs produced by this method to produce better control systems incorporating ratio, split-range and select/over-ride control loops. However, a systematic approach to deriving workable control systems is presented here.

Inventory control

A process plant does not operate steadily on its own. Plants are dynamic in nature, operating according to their dynamic mass and energy balances, and are subject to numerous disturbances. The disturbances come from feed variations, ambient changes, utility variations, and the operators of the plant making their adjustments.

The multitude of balances and relations describing the operation of the plant can be mathematically expressed in lumped-parameter form as follows:

$$dx/dt = f(x, u, d) \tag{D.1}$$

The following observations can be made:
1. "Complete" process control would involve control of every state variable or inventory x_i. This is seldom possible for one or more of the following reasons:
   (a) inability or unacceptable cost of obtaining a measurement of the inventory x_i;
   (b) a lack of manipulated variables u_i or "degrees of freedom";
   (c) control loops which are otherwise possible can be impractical because of lack of sensitivity, slow dynamics, or interactions with other control loops.
   Therefore a selection of the state variables is made and termed the controlled variables.
2. The dimension of the vector u defines the "degrees of freedom" or the maximum number of single control loops possible.
3. The effects on the process of the disturbance variables d_i and the variables u_i not chosen as controlling variables should be minimised. This eases the task of the control system, even in the unlikely case of "complete" control.

It follows that the logical approach is now to:
1. select the controlled variables, a subset of x;
2. select a manipulated variable u_i for each controlled variable x_i;
3. check for control loop interactions, both interactions between x_i and other x_is and between x_i and other u_is;

4. reduce the effects of the remaining independent variables, u_i and d_i;
5. maintain mass inventories first, then energy inventories. This is important in determining the selection of controlled variables made in Point 1 above.

Of course, the above process cannot be completed on a once-through pass and usually several iterations are required, often involving a re-evaluation of the process design.

Selecting controlled variables

The number of state variables for any process is usually quite large, even for the simplest of processes. As discussed previously, control of every state variable is often not achievable or necessary. Hence a selection of the state variables to be controlled has to be made.

The following guidelines may assist in the selection of controlled variables:

Guidelines
1. Always select state variables representing inventories which are not self-regulatory. These state variables can be quickly identified by noting from Equation D.1 those equations in x_i which do not have a term on the right-hand side involving x_i. These variables are not self-regulating.
2. Always select state variables which, although self-regulatory, may exceed equipment or process constraints.
3. Always select state variables which, although self-regulatory, may seriously interact with other inventories.

Areas of particular importance are those where the process interactions are strong, for example in chemical reactions, and where the number of interactions are large, for example in utility supply systems.

An example of a strong interaction is that between the energy inventory and the reaction product inventory in a chemical reactor. Any fluctuations in temperature would markedly affect the reaction rate, which would in turn affect the reactant product concentration.

An example of many interactions is a steam boiler supplying a large plant. The steam pressure (vapor inventory) is self-regulatory, but the fluctuations would affect all steam users.

It is worth emphasizing that this analysis has been limited to single-loop methods. Additional non-interacting controllers could be added, or multivariable control methods used, to control processes that exhibit serious interactions between variables.

Should the number of controlled variables exceed the available number of manipulated variables, only those selected under Guidelines 2 and 3 should be reconsidered.

Selection of manipulated variables

Once the desired number of controlled variables has been chosen from the state variables, it is necessary to select the same number of manipulated variables.

The pairing of manipulated variables with controlled variables was first discussed in a quantitative manner by Bristol (1966) using the Relative Gain Array method. This method, although useful, becomes unwieldy for large systems, and more importantly, only considers steady-state information. Johnston and Barton (1984) have reviewed alternative methods and developed a method that incorporates dynamic information. Johnston, Barton and Brisk (1983) have also examined the question of pairing manipulated and controlled variables using only structural information as opposed to quantitative cause and effect data.

This work attempts to incorporate current design practice with the theoretical work described previously. A selection must be made from the u_i which appear on the right-hand side of Equation 1 (direct action), or a u_i on the right-hand side of another equation, for x_j, where x_j appears on the right-hand side of the equation for x_i (indirect action). The following guidelines can form a basis on which to make the selection:

Guidelines

4. *Direct action* Where possible, choose a variable directly involved in the balance under consideration, rather than one in another balance which acts by interaction between state variables; that is a u_i rather than via an x_j. Direct action is a general rule for total mass balances but in heat and component balances indirect action must often be used.

5. *Sensitivity* The value of the gain between manipulated and controlled variable should be as large as possible. This guideline is usually satisfied by selecting major inflows or outflows, mass or energy, of the balance. In addition, split-range control using two manipulated variables can often improve the sensitivity of control action upon the controlled variable.

6. *Speed of response* Any delays or lags associated with a possible manipulated variable should be small compared with the state-variable time constant.

7. *Interactions with other balances* The extent of interactions with other balances should be minimised. This was the aim of the theoretical work started by Bristol (1966).

8. *Recycling of disturbances* It is preferable to choose an outlet stream which gets rid of the disturbances or a utility stream which is designed to absorb disturbances. Inlet streams effectively recycle the disturbance and should be avoided where possible. This guideline has often been expressed as "pass your disturbances downstream".

In very simple cases it may be possible to find an independent variable which satisfies all of these criteria but in general this is not possible. The relative importance of each condition must be considered and the best compromise selected as the manipulated variable. Even so, when the next step of examining the overall process is carried out it may be necessary to select a less favourable variable for a particular state for the overall good.

Control loop interactions

In making a systematic examination of the balances involved in a complex process, there is a danger of getting into the situation of "not seeing the forest for the trees". Therefore it is necessary at this stage to pause and take an overall look.

There are a number of areas of possible interaction:

1. *Over control* Has a single manipulated variable been used twice as a controlling variable? For example on drawings where a single stream traverses several sheets, the situation sometimes occurs where it is being manipulated by a control valve at each end.
2. *Recycle streams* A careful look should be taken at all recycle streams with regard to possible recycling of disturbances.
3. *Circulating inventories* An area of trouble, especially with the modern emphasis on recovery and re-use of materials and energy.

The remaining independent variables

Once the selection of controlled and controlling variables is finalized the remaining independent variables must be carefully examined. If they are a possible source of disturbance, some action is desirable to reduce the impact of these disturbances on the control system. This can be done in one of three ways:

1. Equipment design or arrangements can be modified. For example:
   • Vapour lines in climates which experience sudden climatic changes should be shielded or insulated.
   • Buffer storage, though expensive, may sometimes be necessary in integrated plants.
2. Control loops can be installed. The careful control of utility streams and flow control of streams from storage are two examples. In addition, "advanced" control techniques such as feed-forward, cascade, ratio and high/low select methods can be installed.
3. Operating procedures may be specified. A good example is the care often taken to blend feedstocks from different sources to maintain fairly constant component concentrations.

Mass inventory control

The selection of controlled and controlling variables, and the implementation of control for mass inventories, is best approached by considering each independent phase (solid, liquid and vapor) for each unit operation in turn. This is achieved by writing *qualitative* mass balances for each unit operation and then applying the guidelines outlined in the previous sections.

The selection of controlled variables for mass inventory control is influenced by three normal process engineering practices:

1. the use of mechanical energy rather than gravity to move materials;
2. the minimizing of vessel size;
3. the relatively small design margins on pressure vessels.

The first practice means that most liquid and solid inventories are not self-regulatory and therefore must be controlled. The other two practices mean that self-regulatory inventories must also be controlled, as constraint violation can easily occur. As a result of these engineering practices, all state variables in solid, liquid, and vapor mass balances should be considered candidates for selection as controlled variables.

The measurements used as an indication of the inventories are generally the level of liquids, the level or weight of solids and the pressure of gases or vapors.

Energy inventory control

Energy inventory control should only be developed after all appropriate mass inventories are controlled.

The first step is to identify the major energy flows within the process and write overall qualitative dynamic energy balances between the major sources and sinks of the energy flows. These balances, in contrast to those developed for mass inventory control, will usually encompass a complete unit operation, or in many cases several unit operations.

Energy inventories are always self-regulatory, but equipment and process constraints may dictate their selection as controlled variables (that is, Guideline 2). Interactions, particularly with mass inventories as a result of phase changes or chemical reactions, are also important (Guideline 3). Selection of controlling variables is governed by the guidelines discussed previously.

Example

An example of the inventory control system resulting from the systematic approach to control system design presented in this paper is shown in Figure A.1. The process is one used by a number of other workers to demonstrate control system design (Douglas 1981, Stephanopoulos 1984).

The derivation of the control system using the approach outlined here is shown in Addendum 1.

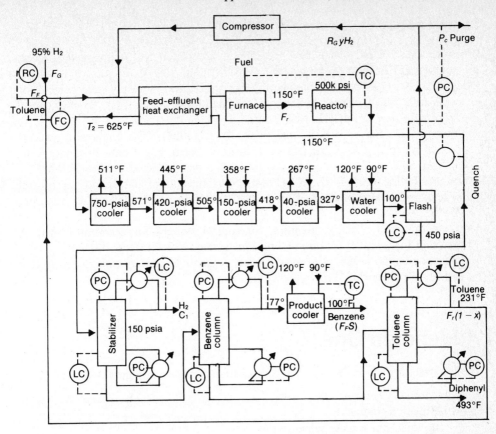

Figure A.1 Example of control system design

Summary

A systematic approach to control system design to maintain steady inventory control has been developed. The approach uses information contained in qualitative mass and energy balances. The approach also relies upon guidelines developed through plant operating experience. An example of the technique applied to a process plant is also presented. The control system produced by this method, although entirely feasible, is usually modified by experienced practitioners to produce a better overall design. This Appendix also provides useful directions for future theoretical developments.

References

Bristol, E. H. (1966), "On a new measure of interaction for multivariable process control", *IEEE Trans. Auto. Control*, AC-11 (1), pp. 133-4.

Douglas, J. M. (1981), "A preliminary design procedure for steady-state control for complete chemical plants", in Seborg, D. E. and Edgar, T. F. (eds), *Proc. Chemical Process Control II*, AICHE, New York.

Johnston, R. D., Barton, G. W., and Brisk, M. L. (1983), "The synthesis of process control systems", *Chemeca-83 Proc.*, 11th Aust. Chem. Eng. Conf., Brisbane, Aust. pp. 595-603.

Johnston, R. D., Barton, G. W. (1984), "Qualification of interactions in control systems", *Chemeca-84 Proc.*, 12th Aust. Chem. Eng. Conf., Melbourne, Aust, pp. 735-42.

Stephanopoulos, G. (1983), "Synthesis of control systems for chemical plants—A challenge for creativity", *Comput. and Chem. Eng.*, Vol. 7 (4), pp. 331-65.

Stephanopoulos, G. (1984), *Chemical process control-An introduction to theory and practice,* Prentice Hall, Englewood Cliffs, NJ.

Addendum One

The following derivation describes the control strategy shown in Figure A.1.

1. *Mass inventory control*
    (a) Distillation columns
        (i) Liquid-phase mass balance:

$$d(\text{accum})/dt = \text{feed} - \text{bottoms} - \text{boil-up} + \text{reflux}$$

Choose this variable as a controlled variable as it is non self-regulatory (Guideline 1). Use level in the bottom of the column as a measure of this variable.

Choose the bottom product flowrate as the controlling variable as it is direct acting (Guideline 4) and passes disturbances downstream (Guideline 8).

Reject the other variables as possible manipulated variables because:

Feed   slow speed of response due to hydraulic delays on trays (Guideline 6);

Boil-up   indirect action through energy inventory (Guideline 4);

Reflux   same as feed.

        (ii) Vapor-phase mass balance:

$$d(\text{accum})/dt = \text{Boil-up} - \text{Condensation}$$

Choose this variable as a controlled variable as it may exceed equipment and process constraints (Guideline 2). Use pressure in the column as a measure of this inventory.

Choose the condensation rate as the controlling variable as it is manipulating a utility stream (Guideline 8). Note though, that it is not direct acting (Guideline 4).

Reject Boil-up as the controlling variable as it is both slow (Guideline 6) and indirect (Guideline 4).

(b) Distillation column accumulator drum
Liquid-phase mass balance:

$$d(\text{accum})/dt = \text{Condensation} - \text{Reflux} - \text{Product}$$

Choose this variable as a controlled variable as it is not self-regulatory (Guideline 1). Use level in the drum as a measure of this inventory.

Choose the product flowrate as a controlling variable as it is direct acting (Guideline 4) and passes disturbances downstream (Guideline 8).

Reject the other variables as manipulated variables because:
Reflux   recycles disturbances (Guideline 8);
Condensation   interacts with other balances (Guideline 7).

(c) Distillation column reboilers
  (i) Vapor-phase mass balance:

$$d(\text{accum})/dt = \text{inlet steam} - \text{condensing rate}$$

Choose this variable as a controlled variable as it may exceed equipment and process constraints (Guideline 2). It is self-regulatory. A measure of this inventory is the pressure on the shell-side of the reboiler.

Choose the inlet steam flowrate as the controlling variable as it is both direct acting (Guideline 4) and is a utility stream (Guideline 8).

Reject the condensing rate as a possible controlling variable as it interacts with the energy inventory (Guideline 7).
  (ii) Liquid-phase mass balance:

$$d(\text{accum})/dt = \text{Condensing rate} - \text{Condensate}$$

Choose this variable as a controlled variable as, although it is self-regulatory, it may exceed equipment and process constraints (Guideline 2).

Choose the condensate flowrate as the controlling variable as it is both direct acting (Guideline 4) and passes disturbances downstream (Guideline 8).

Reject the condensing rate as a possible controlling variable as it interacts with the energy inventory (Guideline 7).
Note: This is not shown in Figure 1. This is because this loop is conventionally implemented with a steam-trap.

(d) Flash drum
  (i) Liquid-phase mass balance:

$$d(\text{accum})/dt = \text{feed} - \text{bottoms} - \text{flashed}$$

Choose this variable as a controlled variable as it is not self-regulatory (Guideline 1). A measure of this inventory is the level in the flash drum.

Choose the bottom liquid flowrate as the controlling variable as it is direct acting (Guideline 4) and passes disturbances downstream (Guideline 8).

Reject the other variables as possible manipulated variables because:

Feed   recycles disturbances (Guideline 8);

Flashed   indirect action (Guideline 4) through energy inventory.

(ii) Vapor-phase mass balance

$$d(\text{accum})/dt = \text{flashed} - \text{recycle} - \text{purge}$$

Choose this variable as a controlled variable as it may exceed equipment and process constraints (Guideline 2). A measure of this inventory is the pressure in the flash drum.

Choose the purge flowrate as the controlling variable as it is direct acting (Guideline 4) and passes disturbances downstream (Guideline 8). Note that this stream may be quite a small flowrate and thus insensitive (Guideline 5 violation).

Reject the other variables as possible controlling variables because:

Flashed   acts indirectly through energy inventory (Guideline 4);

Recycle   recycle disturbances (Guideline 8).

Note: If the recycle stream was chosen as the controlling variable and it was decided to flow-control the purge flowrate, there would be no control over the inventory of hydrogen within the total process. This is an even stronger reason for choosing the purge flowrate as the controlling variable and further enforces Guideline 8.

2. *Remaining independent variables.* Having completed the design of the mass inventory control scheme, and before designing an energy inventory control scheme, an inspection of the flowsheet reveals a number of remaining independent variables. These are:

• toluene and hydrogen flows;

• recycle quench flowrate.

These variables could act as sources of disturbances and should be controlled if possible. It is also desirable to control the ratio of hydrogen to toluene in the feed stream.

Therefore, the following control loops are added:

(a) flow-control the recycle quench flowrate;

(b) ratio control the hydrogen feed flowrate to the toluene feed flowrate;

(c) flow control the combined toluene plus hydrogen feed flowrate by manipulating the toluene flowrate.

3. *Energy inventory control.*

(a) Furnace/reactor system

Major energy sources: Fuel to furnace;

                               Energy from exothermic reaction.

Major energy sink: Product from reactor.

$$d(\text{accum})/dt = \text{Fuel enthalpy} + \text{heat of reaction} - \text{product enthalpy}$$

Choose this variable as a controlled variable even though it is self-regulatory as equipment and process constraints may be exceeded (Guideline 2) and serious interactions with the mass inventory may occur (Guideline 3).

Choose the fuel flowrate as the controlling variable as it is direct acting (Guideline 4) and it is a utility stream (Guideline 8).

Reject the product flowrate as a possible manipulated variable as it interacts with mass inventory (Guideline 7) and more importantly it would represent over-control.

Reject the heat of reaction as a possible controlling variable as it interacts with the reaction product mass inventory (Guideline 7).

Note: The exit stream from the reactor was chosen for the measurement rather than the inlet stream to reactor (which is the exit from the furnace). The latter would not detect changes caused by the uncontrolled energy input to the balance, namely the heat of reaction.

(b) Water cooler

Major source: Product to cooler train.

Major sink: Cooling water to water cooler.

$$d(\text{accum})/dt = \text{Product enthalpy} - \text{cooling water enthalpy}$$

Choose this variable as a controlled variable even though it is self-regulatory as processing constraints may be violated (Guideline 2) and it may interact with the mass inventory (Guideline 3).

Choose the cooling water flowrate as the controlling variable as it is direct acting (Guideline 4) and is a utility stream (Guideline 8).

Reject product enthalpy as a controlling variable as it interacts with the mass inventory (Guideline 7) and it would result in over-control.

(c) Benzene product cooler

Major source: Benzene product stream.

Major sink: Cooling water.

$$d(\text{accum})/dt = \text{Product enthalpy} - \text{cooling water enthalpy}$$

Choose this variable as a controlled variable even though it is self-regulatory as processing constraints may be violated (Guideline 2).

Choose the cooling water flowrate as the controlling variable as it is direct acting (Guideline 4) and is a utility stream (Guideline 8).

Reject benzene product enthalpy as a possible controlling variable as it interacts with the mass inventory (Guideline 7) and it would result in over-control.

Appendix E:
Relation matrix for fuzzy evaporator model

The relation matrix takes the following form:

$$RM(U_n, Y_{n-1}, Y_n)$$

so that the seven square matrices listed below represent $RM(U_n, Y_{n-1}, *)$ for each of the fuzzy reference sets represented in Y_n.

In each square matrix the rows represent $RM(U_n, *, *)$ and the columns $RM(*, Y_{n-1}, *)$.

Matrix $RM(U_n, Y_{n-1}, *)$ for Y_n set 1

0.0726	0.0443	0.0000	0.0000	0.0000	0.0000	0.0000
0.0000	0.0000	0.0000	0.0000	0.0000	0.0000	0.0000
0.0000	0.0000	0.0000	0.0000	0.0000	0.0000	0.0000
0.0000	0.0000	0.0000	0.0000	0.0000	0.0000	0.0000
0.0000	0.0000	0.0000	0.0000	0.0000	0.0000	0.0000
0.0000	0.0000	0.0000	0.0000	0.0000	0.0000	0.0000
0.0000	0.0000	0.0000	0.0000	0.0000	0.0000	0.0000

Matrix $RM(U_n, Y_{n-1}, *)$ for Y_n set 2

0.0979	0.0477	0.0000	0.0000	0.0000	0.0000	0.0000
0.5077	0.4423	0.4516	0.4046	0.4336	0.4029	0.4198
0.2169	0.3357	0.0000	0.0000	0.0656	0.0000	0.0184
0.1445	0.1648	0.0000	0.0000	0.0313	0.0000	0.0000
0.0000	0.0000	0.0000	0.0000	0.0000	0.0000	0.0000
0.0000	0.0000	0.0000	0.0000	0.0000	0.0000	0.0000
0.0000	0.0000	0.0000	0.0000	0.0000	0.0000	0.0000

Matrix RM(U_n, Y_{n-1}, *) for Y_n set 3

0.0258	0.0248	0.0000	0.0000	0.0000	0.0000	0.0000
0.4884	0.5301	0.4797	0.4046	0.4510	0.4625	0.4979
0.6280	0.4961	0.3365	0.4945	0.3909	0.2429	0.4610
0.6373	0.5045	0.0020	0.0021	0.0656	0.0714	0.0009
0.2873	0.3175	0.0590	0.0116	0.0656	0.0714	0.0011
0.0000	0.0000	0.0000	0.0000	0.0000	0.0000	0.0000
0.0000	0.0000	0.0000	0.0000	0.0000	0.0000	0.0000

Matrix RM(U_n, Y_{n-1}, *) for Y_n set 4

0.0000	0.0000	0.0000	0.0000	0.0000	0.0000	0.0000
0.0001	0.0714	0.1482	0.1134	0.1017	0.1399	0.1399
0.0054	0.5000	0.4929	0.5186	0.5098	0.4981	0.5213
0.0856	0.4826	0.4990	0.4729	0.5718	0.4269	0.2916
0.6308	0.5129	0.4761	0.3858	0.4691	0.4269	0.0078
0.0810	0.2346	0.1530	0.2309	0.1411	0.2511	0.0157
0.0122	0.0000	0.0000	0.0000	0.0000	0.0000	0.0000

Matrix RM(U_n, Y_{n-1}, *) for Y_n set 5

0.0000	0.0000	0.0000	0.0000	0.0000	0.0000	0.0000
0.0000	0.0000	0.0000	0.0000	0.0000	0.0000	0.0000
0.0000	0.0000	0.0149	0.0639	0.0927	0.1536	0.1829
0.0773	0.0002	0.4809	0.5189	0.1632	0.4808	0.5106
0.0773	0.4856	0.4963	0.6042	0.6806	0.5362	0.3674
0.5612	0.5070	0.5230	0.5633	0.6254	0.4880	0.0316
0.1718	0.1905	0.3213	0.2581	0.3547	0.0658	0.0134

Matrix RM(U_n, Y_{n-1}, *) for Y_n set 6

0.0000	0.0000	0.0000	0.0000	0.0000	0.0000	0.0000
0.0000	0.0000	0.0000	0.0000	0.0000	0.0000	0.0000
0.0000	0.0000	0.0000	0.0000	0.0000	0.0000	0.0000
0.0000	0.0000	0.0000	0.0000	0.0336	0.1428	0.1428
0.0058	0.0185	0.0048	0.0009	0.0656	0.4269	0.5158
0.1604	0.4442	0.3655	0.3108	0.2693	0.4269	0.5636
0.5271	0.4943	0.5388	0.5461	0.4559	0.5017	0.4549

Matrix RM(U_n, Y_{n-1}, *) for Y_n set 7

0.0000	0.0000	0.0000	0.0000	0.0000	0.0000	0.0000
0.0000	0.0000	0.0000	0.0000	0.0000	0.0000	0.0000
0.0000	0.0000	0.0000	0.0000	0.0000	0.0000	0.0000
0.0000	0.0000	0.0000	0.0000	0.0000	0.0000	0.0000
0.0000	0.0000	0.0000	0.0000	0.0000	0.0441	0.0246
0.0050	0.1053	0.0002	0.0071	0.0656	0.1901	0.0997
0.4721	0.3375	0.4516	0.3131	0.3925	0.4269	0.5019

Index

adaptive control,　73–9
autocorrelations,　21–2, 24–8

constraint control,　92–6
constraints,　92–5, 134

damping ratio,　16
data collection,　14–15
deadtime compensation,　66–72
decay ratio,　51
decoupling,　46–52, 53, 115, 134
defuzzifier,　102
degrees of freedom,　11, 55, 92–3, 133
differencing,　21, 22
DMC,　80, 86, 113

equation
　discrete,　2–3
　output,　2, 59, 60–1
　state,　2, 12, 59, 60–1
evaporator
　degrees of freedom,　11
　diagram,　7
　Jacobians,　12
　linear model,　12–13, 55, 60
　model implementations,　11
　nonlinear model,　9–11
　steady state,　8
　step tests,　17–19
　time series model,　24–30
　variables,　8, 13

feasible operating space,　92–4
feedforward,　39–45, 115, 116–117
frequency content,　15, 16
fuzzifier,　101
fuzzy control,　97, 101–6, 107, 109–12
fuzzy identification,　107–9
fuzzy sets,　97–104

gain scheduling,　73–5, 93
generic model control,　113–17, 120

heuristic,　93, 97, 101–6, 107

identification,　14 31, 76, 107–9
IMC,　113, 114
impulse responses,　22–3, 26
integral action,　54, 93, 94, 104, 114–15
interactions,　35–8, 44, 46, 115, 133–7
inventory control,　32–3, 118–19, 132–42
ISE measure,　42–4, 70
ITAE measure,　74, 89, 120

Jacobians,　2, 12, 127–8

Kalman filter,　59–65

Laplace transform,　4
lead-lag compensator,　40–1
least-squares estimation,　21, 23–4, 76–7
linear multivariable regulator,　53–8
loop pairing,　37–8, 115, 118–19, 133, 135–6

matrix
　control,　2, 12
　discrete,　3
　disturbance,　2, 12
　dynamic,　82
　relation,　100, 102, 103, 105, 143–4
　state,　2, 12
model
　ARIMA,　20–1
　ARMA,　76
　convolution,　80–2, 85
　empirical,　1, 14–31
　fitting,　14, 17, 23–30